Survival is...

THE ULTIMATE DEFIANCE

Susan Young is a writer and photographer living in South Devon with her husband and her golden retriever. Her previous books have been technical. Her photographs she hopes are artistic. Her love of nature is profound.

THE ULTIMATE DEFIANCE

Susan Young

OxPens

First published in Great Britain 2010
by WritersPrintShop

ISBN 9781904623136 8

Designed by Keith Hodgson www.antcreative.com

This book is based on fact, inspired by the story of the real life Halina, who generously gave me her time and told me of the painful events in her past. I now regard her as a dear friend and hope I have done justice to her and her family.

Some minor events have been fictionalised to fill the gaps left by time, but I have tried to be as authentic as possible. The miracles really did take place.

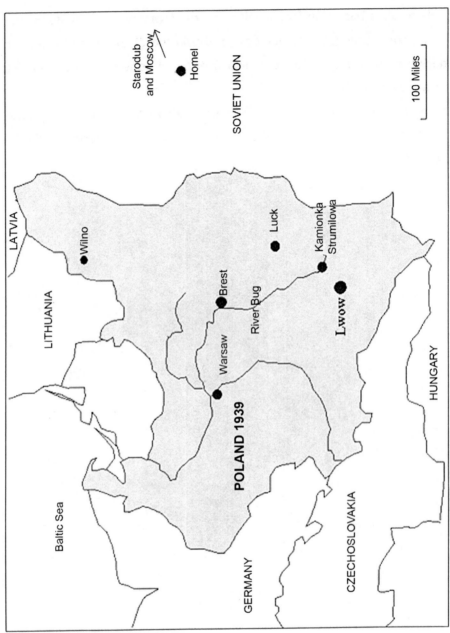

1. Poland 1939 before the invasions

Prologue

Halina aged 11 with Ola aged 7.
'The happy memories of childhood...'

Halina, January 2010, Devon, England

The happy memories of childhood are there, waiting in the bright summer sun that always shines in childhood past. Now and then, I catch a glimpse of them, but I dare not travel towards them - to go that way I have to pass through those other areas stalked by nightmares.

At night however, memories are freer. If I am lucky, I can flit past the terrors and alight on a moment remembered - the excitement of hiding on the stairs as Mama plays the piano and sings. I reach out and almost touch her hair.

Then the moment is gone.

Even in dreams, memories are fleeting, a moment stolen and quickly replaced.

Just in case.

Just in case the nightmares catch a hint of my pleasure and gallop towards me with hooves thudding and manes flying, bringing back the darkness.

I wrote that passage on the ship over to England after the war, when my memories were still fresh and painful. At that time, I like so many others, just wanted to forget, but now I feel I must tell my story, for my daughter, and for others whose parents and grandparents found their experiences too terrible to describe.

If I succeed, my daughter, and those other sons and daughters, will understand what we went through, but it is difficult to paint a picture of just how awful the conditions were, and because they did not undergo the experience, they may find it hard to imagine. What experience do they have that will give a real insight into the horrors? The worst most have suffered is a power cut, a night without electricity. How can they imagine days, weeks, months, and years without adequate heat, light, food, water, clothes, and shelter? How can they feel the despair that many felt when stripped of almost all that defines life?

Often people ask how I survived, how I kept sane. All I can say is that I was young and adaptable and had not yet experienced the true joys of life and love. I could not mourn what I had not lost. In addition, I had spirit. I had the unbounded zest for life owned by the young and innocent. Somehow the wounds did not cut so deep and were more quickly healed.

The story of these horrors is almost unknown in Britain. Many know that Germany invaded Poland from the West, causing Britain to go to war, but few are aware that at the same time, Soviet Russia invaded Poland from the East and systematically set about destroying our way of life. Many found it too difficult to tell of those terrible times, which is one reason that I write now. Perhaps it is easier for me - my memories are softened with that intense feeling of joy when… but that is at the end. I must begin at the beginning, before Poland was torn apart.

ONE

Kazimierz 1939.
' Papa could look very severe at times............
once he warmed up he was quite sweet
really.'

The Korbinski family, July 1939,
Eastern Poland

'It is time you learned how to swim.'

Halina awoke from her daydream with a start, to find her mother standing over her blocking out the sun.

'Time you learned how to swim,' she repeated.

'But where?' Halina looked over towards the fast-flowing river on her left. 'There?' she said, trying to control the nervousness in her voice.

'No, in the pool further up,' said Eugenia with a glint in her eye, 'or are you afraid?'

'Of course not!' Halina jumped to her feet, with a conviction that she did not feel, and walked slowly along the riverbank, watching the water rushing past and swirling round pebbles and boulders. It was moving at great speed. She might be carried off downstream and end up as a limp bundle on some muddy beach miles away. She looked at the pool her mother was indicating. It was quite deep, but the water was moving more slowly, which was a relief. She stood on the bank hesitating. Her father was sitting further along the bank, his feet dipping in and out of the water as he swung his legs to and fro. Halina glanced at him and the task ahead took on a new dimension. Papa could not swim, he would be very jealous if she succeeded. It would annoy him a great deal. That was worth some effort.

She ran into the water, holding her breath as the cold shocked her. She dare not let her apprehension show. For quarter of an hour she splashed and gurgled and spluttered, flailing arms and legs in an uncoordinated fashion, with her mother standing by giving instructions, and holding her under the chin from time to time. Suddenly she got everything right. She was swimming.

'I did it,' Halina shouted to her mother, as finally she pulled herself dripping and shivering from the water straight into the towel being held in front of her.

'I never doubted you would,' Eugenia said, and smiled at her daughter fondly. 'Well done Halina. You have learned very quickly.' She noticed her husband had risen to his feet and was coming towards them.

'Hasn't Halina done well,' she beamed, rubbing Halina's back hard until it glowed and she forgot how cold the water had been.

Halina glanced at her father, who was trying to appear encouraging, but his smile looked strained. She realised that he was ashamed now she could swim whereas he could not. She had beaten him. He would not live it down if the men he commanded found out. However, as she saw him looking uncharacteristically sheepish, somehow her triumph no longer seemed so sweet.

The summer holiday in the Carpathian Mountains was one of the few times that her family was together. That in itself was a reason to celebrate, but the wonderful majestic sweep of the mountains completed the feeling of excitement Halina always felt when in their midst. The tree-covered slopes, cut at intervals by narrow clefts, were washed by rivers that ran to the flower-covered meadows beneath. That afternoon, after her swimming triumph, she sat among the flowers with Ola, her younger sister, making necklaces and crowns, competing with her to see who had the greater number of different flowers in each garland. At fifteen she was really too old for garland making, but the magic of the place overwhelmed her, and the years fell away like so many layers.

As she sat with the warm alpine sun on her face, she recalled the first holiday there when she was eleven. She had a room facing up the mountain, which rose so steeply above the hotel that all she could see was grass. Eugenia complained that it was not a good room and that she should have one at the front.

'I do not know why you could not share with Ola,' she said, 'she has a good room and I am sure they would put in another bed for you.'

'Really Mama,' Halina replied, 'I love this room. Besides, Ola snores.'

'She does not!' said her mother, laughing, but she understood that her daughter was coming to the age when privacy started to matter a great deal, and so she let the matter rest.

What she did not know of was Halina's morning excursions. On the afternoon they arrived, Halina looked out of her window and noticed a flat roof an easy step away. The roof had walls on two sides, and a short drop to the ground on a third side. The remaining side was the one in which she was interested. That edge of the flat roof was built into the hillside, and by walking on it, she would be able to climb up the hill. She studied the lie of the land for some minutes, and decided it was worth a try. She would have to wait until early morning just about sunrise, when there would be no one about and she would not be disturbed. It just would not do for an officer's daughter to be seen climbing out of windows and running about on hillsides.

4

The first morning she awoke just at the right time. The sun was not yet up, but it was light enough to see clearly. She pulled hard at the window to open it. The hotel was old and the window quite stiff, but with a bit of effort it opened with a squeak. She held her breath. She must make sure no one had heard. They would probably think nothing of it, as the old hotel had lots of squeaks and creaks but she should wait just in case. After a few minutes of silence, she put one leg over the windowsill and lowered it gingerly onto the roof. There was always the possibility that the roof would collapse and she would suffer a terrible injury. She smiled to herself. That would cause a commotion. She crept across the roof and jumped onto the grass beyond. One foot slipped in the dew-wet grass and she grazed a knee, but she held onto tufts of grass and safely clambered up the slope.

She walked up the hill, using her hands to push herself up on the steepest parts. She kept climbing until she reached a large flat stone and sitting on it, turned to look at the hill below her. Although she had climbed only a hundred feet, the hotel had almost disappeared. Over the tops of the village roofs, the mountains on the other side of the valley were becoming visible as the sun started to rise. Behind the first ridge, she could see further ridges fading into the dark blue distance. Everything was newly washed with dew - fresh and young and not yet aged by the heat of the day. She sat on the stone with the early, tender, sun on her face, drinking in the quiet stillness of the morning. This was how it felt to be the only person in the world. She dare not move in case she broke the spell.

Suddenly the banging of a door and the clattering of pots shattered the quiet, as the kitchen staff got to work in the hotel. The magic of the moment had evaporated. She slipped and ran down the hill and hastily climbed back in the window and closed it. Not a moment too soon, as only five minutes later, her mother knocked on the door and came in just as she had finished washing her knee and hiding the evidence of her outing.

'Breakfast will soon be ready, Halina.'

Halina walked behind her mother along the passageway and suddenly felt a start of alarm. Her shoes were still wet with dew. What if Papa noticed?

'Mine is much better than yours!'

Halina returned to the present with a start and realised that Ola was speaking to her. She looked at the garland her sister was brandishing in front of her, and saw that she had not finished her own.

'You are always daydreaming these days,' pouted Ola, echoing the phrase she had so often heard her father say to her sister.

'I am thinking of great things,' Halina retorted, not wanting to admit the truth. That carefree time of several years ago seemed so long ago now. She still anticipated the holidays eagerly, but she longed for those times of innocence. Now, she felt that her relationship with her father had become strained. He was an officer in the Polish army and moved to different parts of eastern Poland every few years. She knew that he taught young soldiers who were training to be officers, but why did he not realise that he should treat young girls differently? And why did he have to be so strict? It was not necessary to be as strict.

She loved her father as a daughter should, but she did not always like him. She had not noticed it as much when she had been younger, and anxious for his approval. Then

5

she had been compliant, rather as Ola was now, but she resented his discipline these days. Every time she tried to assert herself and show Papa that she was grown up, he sent her to her room in disgrace. She impatiently dashed away a tear. It still upset her when he punished her, and as soon as she was alone, her soft centre would bubble up, washed out by her tears. Why did he still affect her that way? Even after her swimming triumph, Papa did not seem to realise that she was strong and independent. It had been a hollow victory and still she had that familiar feeling of emptiness. If only Papa would show his love more often.

August 1939, Kamionka Strumilowa

Ola waited in the hall until the maid had left the study. She was carrying her father's boots and his spare uniform for cleaning, which meant she would be gone for a while. She knocked on the study door and entered. Her father was sitting at his desk surrounded by papers, and scarcely acknowledged her presence.

'Papa can you help me with my history?' she asked, 'I have a test when I go back to school after the holidays.' She gauged from his expression that he was about to say he was too busy, so she added quickly, 'I am quite a long way behind because I started a different book when we moved here, and Sabina Milewska is better than me. If I do not manage to catch up, I will no longer be top of the class.'

Her father turned and beckoned to her, 'Well, we cannot have that, can we,' he said, motioning her to sit on the chair beside him.

An hour later Ola emerged from her father's study, having successfully moved from Poland in 1850 to telling her father about her exploits at school and that she had decided she wanted to study medicine at Lwow University. 'I do like art very much,' she had said, 'but realise that it will not give me a good career.' This last was not quite true, but she knew it is what her father would want to hear.

She closed the door quietly behind her. Papa could look very severe at times, especially when he was working, but she just had to take a deep breath, and think of the right thing to say. Anything to do with schoolwork would get his full attention, and that comment she had made about Sabina Milewska had been a masterstroke. It was not quite true, as she was much better at history than Sabina, but Papa would never know that. Just let him think that he had helped her to get top marks in Polish history.

She started to climb the stairs. It was a shame she could not get his attention without having to try so hard, but at least she got it. Besides, once he warmed up he was quite sweet really. Today she had even given him a kiss before she left. She frowned a little. His cheek had been a bit wet and it looked like he had tears in his eyes, but she must have imagined that. Papa would never cry. He was too brave and strong. She opened the door to her room to put away her schoolbooks. She did not know why Halina complained that Papa had no time for her. She just did not use the right technique.

Eugenia adjusted the silk shawl round her shoulders and took one last look in the mirror to ensure that she was presentable. She was a beautiful woman with the kind of elegance that everyone noticed. She was tall and slim with a curtain of dark hair that swung from side to side as she moved. However, it was her eyes that people noticed, eyes that hypnotised everyone. They were huge, dark and lustrous. 'Gypsy eyes,' Kazimierz would say to tease her. She was modest about the reaction she had on people, but still enjoyed the little extra attention she received. To be the wife of a Polish army officer was the dream of many young girls and she counted herself lucky that she had achieved it. To be thought of as beautiful was a bonus.

Tonight they were entertaining the Mirons – the parents of Halina's school friend Adela. Mr Miron was a civil engineer and the couple lived in a modest house on the other side of Kamionka. He had an injury and was not eligible for the army, but that did not bother him until he visited Eugenia and Kazimierz. Eugenia sighed a little. The evening would be one dominated by stories of the army. Staszek Miron lived the army life vicariously through Kazimierz, and the stories of Kazimierz' exploits defeating the Soviets in 1920 would be told yet again. Her husband was not one to boast, but such an encouraging audience fired his patriotic fervour.

She really had little in common with Veronica Miron. Veronica was a pleasant, mousy woman who had lived all her life in Kamionka, whereas she had travelled throughout Poland with Kazimierz, and had entertained generals, mayors and other dignitaries. It was all too obvious at times how much better educated she was than Veronica - she even spoke Russian quite fluently. In comparison, Veronica was limited in her outlook and was animated only when talking about her cooking – a fact borne out by her figure, which tended to spill out over her dresses. Eugenia smoothed her skirt and smiled. What would Veronica say if she knew that she left much of the cooking to her maid when she entertained? Not that she usually admitted it. Tonight would be more of a trial than usual, as it would be overshadowed by talk of the situation in Europe, and whether there would be a war with Germany. She put her shawl back on the chair – she would not need it on such a warm night - and made her way downstairs to receive her guests.

Halina watched her mother leave, and crept into the room. She picked up the silken shawl and put it round her shoulders. She swung from side to side, imagining the rustle of the long skirts of an evening gown, as she had done on many occasions before. Mama would not mind. She had caught sight of her once, standing in the doorway with a fond smile as she watched the make believe. Halina smiled at her reflection in the mirror. It was exciting whenever Mama dressed up for dinner. She always wore such beautiful dresses and asked for her opinion, which made her feel quite adult. It was as if she were the mother, and Mama the child. 'Does the dress look good?' she had said, dancing in front of her, her eyes even more lustrous than usual, twirling this way and that for approval.

Tonight's dinner party was to be a modest affair, and Mama's dress one of her simpler gowns. Not like the last ball dress she had worn. 'This is a backless dress,' Mama had said, 'Dark blue silk and very daring.' She had tilted her head up a little as if to ward off any disapproval, of which there was none, of course, but she had pulled her silken shawl more tightly round her shoulders just in case.

That beautiful silken shawl. Halina lifted the shawl to her nose. It always smelled sweetly of Mama's perfume. She hoped the evening would finish as usual with her mother playing the piano to entertain the guests. She thought back fondly to the times when she was younger, and hid on the stairs with Ola to listen to Mama as she sat at the piano. Best of all were those memorable evenings in Lwow, when a family friend brought his violin. Mama played the piano, accompanied by the violin, and Papa sang. They opened the windows wide at the request of the neighbours, who listened to the impromptu concerts and called for more. Those were wonderful evening of music, but what she remembered with most pleasure, was the sight of Papa smiling and laughing.

Halina replaced the shawl where her mother had left it. Those days seemed to have gone now. Since leaving Lwow two years ago, Papa had become more preoccupied with his work and Mama had lost a little of her sparkle. Why did things have to change?

TWO

The Korbinski family, August 1939, Kamionka Strumilowa

Although Halina had little interest in politics, she started to notice a change in atmosphere in the house. Her parents listened to the radio frequently, and she could tell that something serious was happening.

'Staszek Miron does not believe there will be a war in Europe,' she heard her father say a few days after the dinner party. 'I think he is burying his head in the sand.'

Halina found the thought of war rather exciting at first, and at night, she dreamed of herself as a Polish heroine, vanquishing the enemy and carrying out great deeds of bravery. However, as August wore on, her parents started looking more and more serious. She started listening to the radio with them, and began to realise that her happy fantasies did not bear much relation to reality.

At the end of August, her father was called to his company, and from her mother's sad expression, she knew it was not a social visit.

'What is going on, Mama?' she asked.

Eugenia smiled at her and after looking around to see that Ola was not there, she said, 'Your father thinks there will be a war between Germany and Poland. He has gone on manoeuvres with his company and to meet his general.' She stood up, her face paling as she did, 'Oh Halina, if there is a war, he will have to leave us to go and lead his company. He will have to go.' She sat down again, with tears in her eyes.

Halina knelt in front of her and held her hands. 'Mama,' she said, 'you will have Ola and me. We will look after you.' What she was thinking was how much calmer life would be without her father's strictness to upset her.

Eugenia held on to her daughter's hand and smiled again, but the tears were still there.

September 1939

On the 1st of September, Germany declared war on Poland as feared. Kazimierz came back to tell his family he had to go and join his company in two days time.

The day before he was due to leave, Halina was walking home after visiting her school friend Adela. The girls had little idea what war really meant, and they spent the afternoon sitting in the park talking and giggling, as they watched some young fishermen on the nearby river. On her way back, Halina passed a boy called Edmund who she knew slightly. He was a few years older than she was, but they shared an interest in the Scout movement. Edmund was tall, with a mass of golden brown curls that enhanced his boyish good looks. That day as she passed, she noticed that he was dressed in his scout uniform and was crouching down in front of some sticks. She went up to him and he started to tell her what he had learned at his last scout meeting.

'One of the most important survival techniques is to find shelter and then light a fire. You cannot assume you will have matches. Even if you do they may be wet or scarce, so we are taught these alternative ways of lighting fires.' Edmund had a habit of leaping straight into a topic without any preamble or greeting which Halina found very amusing, but she suppressed a smile. He might be offended if she laughed at him.

'This is an old fashioned tinder box,' he said, taking a small tin box out of his pocket. He opened it and showed her the contents – some fine strips of bark, and a piece of flint. 'This could save your life,' he continued, 'you lay out the bark with any fine, dry grass you can find, and strike the flint with a knife. The sparks that form will ignite the bark and you have your fire. You could try if you like, but you must replace the pieces of bark should you manage to light the fire.'

At that, he raised his head and looked at Halina through his curls. She noticed that he was blushing, which must mean that he liked her. She was very flattered, but took care not to let it show. Adela would be so jealous. She had always liked Edmund.

'I suppose I could have a try,' she said casually. She did not want him to know she was much keener that she pretended. She borrowed his knife and struck the flint repeatedly. After some minutes, she managed to light some pieces of grass. They quickly extinguished, but that was fine, boys did not like it if girls were too successful.

'It takes a lot of practice,' Edmund said, looking impressed, 'but you have made a good start. We can try again next time you are passing, if you like.'

Halina started to walk home and was more than a little surprised when Edmund started to walk home with her, telling her more about his scouting exploits and the many skills he had learned, as they walked. As they approached her garden gate, he fished in his pocket and took out a small piece of flint.

'Here, take this,' he mumbled, his face still a little red, 'you can practice on your own.'

He turned and walked back the way he had come, and Halina opened the gate. Papa might not approve, but once he had gone, she would be able to practice lighting fires in the garden. She came up to the front door, and jumped nervously when her father appeared on the step. She quickly pushed the flint into her pocket.

'I have been watching you from the window,' he said, 'who is that boy and what were you doing?'

'No one and nothing Papa,' she said, 'Edmund was just telling me about the scout movement.'

'You must not go with boys like that, Halina,' he said sternly. 'As an officer's daughter, you must not go about with boys that we do not know.'

Later that evening in her room, Halina sat on her bed, anger boiling inside her at what she saw as the unfairness of her father's words. All she had done was talk. All Edmund had done was to give her a piece of flint. She put her hand in her pocket to touch the flint. It was not there! She could not lose something Edmund had given her. Not after it had caused so much trouble. She would have to get up early next day and look for it before her father left.

Next morning she awoke early, and crept downstairs before anyone else was awake. She opened the back door carefully, as it was inclined to creak, and made her way to the front of the house. The flint had probably dropped out of her pocket near the front door. It should be easier to find there, as there was no long grass. She looked around and found it after a few minutes. A little muddy but that would soon wash off. Now she would not have any awkward explaining if Edmund asked her where it was. She just had breakfast to sit through, and then her father would be gone.

Breakfast was a strained affair. Eugenia was close to tears at the thought of her husband's imminent departure and Ola, who usually mirrored her mother's emotions, was snuffling into her bread. Halina sat resolutely in front of her food, refusing to look anywhere in the direction of her father. As soon as she had eaten, she rushed upstairs, ignoring the cry that she should ask permission before she left the table.

'What will happen to her when I have gone,' Kazimierz said, 'she is so defiant.'

Eugenia lifted her head and looked at her husband. Whenever he spoke in such a way about her daughter, she felt each word slice into her like a knife. 'My dear, do not be too hard on Halina, she does not mean to torment you, she is just trying to grow up and develop her own personality.'

Kazimierz sighed. 'I know, I know, but once I have gone, who will keep her on the right track? I must show her the way.'

Eugenia moved closer and touched her husband on the arm. 'Have faith in her Kazimierz. You do not need to be so strict with her. Your mother told me..,' she faltered, '..your mother told me your father had been very strict with you and you ran away when you were sixteen. As a result, she said you find it hard to show your emotions, but please show Halina you love her before you go. We do not know when we will see you again.' The words came out in a rush as she was saying something she had practised many times, but never before had the courage to say.

Kazimierz was quiet for several moments and Eugenia feared she had gone too far. Finally, he looked at her and she saw the unfamiliar sight of raw emotion in his eyes.

'It is true he was hard on me, but I did not really run away, I just wanted to join the army. However, it is true I was very young at the time. Giena, because I do not think it right to show my emotions, does not mean I do not feel them. I know I have been preoccupied for some time, but as well as the German problem, there has been much Soviet guerrilla activity on the border. We are,' he paused, 'concerned.' He smiled at Eugenia and took her hand, and she felt closer to him than she had for some time.

'Well, I don't think Halina will run off to join the army,' she said, and was relieved to see the tension leave her husband's face.

When it was time for her father to leave, Halina stayed in her bedroom, still angry with him. She was glad he was leaving. Now she would have some peace and would be able to live her life without constant criticism. She sat cross-legged on her bed and folded her arms, and did not move when her mother knocked on the door and entered.

'Halina,' she said, 'why are you not coming to say goodbye to your father. We do not know when we will see him again.'

'I am not going,' Halina replied, 'I do not care.'

Eugenia sat on the bed, 'Halina,' she said, 'please do not be cross with your father today of all days. He does love you, you know, and he is very upset that you are not going to say goodbye. You might regret it if you do not.'

Halina glanced at her mother and saw the beseeching look in her eyes. Mama could be so persuasive, but although that would not sway her, she had said that Papa was upset that she had not said goodbye. Perhaps he did love her after all. Her defiance crumbled. She unfolded her legs and made her way downstairs.

Her father was standing at the door in his uniform waiting to leave, and to her surprise, his face lit up when he saw her. He hugged her tightly and said, 'Look after your mother, Halina.'

The door closed and silence settled like dust. The three stood still for several minutes unable to deal with emotions and move at the same time. Halina was confused and did not know whether she was sad or relieved. She swallowed the lump in her throat. Why she was feeling so emotional? Surely she was glad that he had gone.

Eventually her mother spoke, 'School is starting soon, and we must make sure everything is ready.'

'But there is a war, surely there will be no school,' Halina protested.

'We will be ready,' she replied and purposefully marched up stairs to check through her daughters' school clothes.

THREE

Eugenia, Halina, Ola, September 1939, Kamionka Strumilowa

Later that week, Halina was walking in the park alongside the river with her mother and sister. Ola was walking ahead kicking up the yellow and red autumn leaves lining the path.

'I remember,' she said to her mother, 'when I was little, Papa told me a story about a rich and cruel king who had large hoards of gold and rubies. A witch disguised as a beggar was cruelly treated by him, and turned all his gold and jewels to leaves. She made the leaves fall off the trees every autumn to remind him of what he had lost. I was told that if I looked hard enough I might still find some real gold there.'

Eugenia laughed. 'I remember that story,' she said, 'You would come in every day in autumn with wet leaves covering your shoes and gloves.'

Suddenly they saw some German soldiers on the other side of the river. They were only a few hundred yards away. Eugenia pulled her daughters behind a tree and they peered round the trunk. 'Keep back,' she said, in a harsh tone. Halina regained her position a few minutes later. She did not want to miss anything, whatever Mama said. Several Polish soldiers approached from the other side and there was a series of loud cracks. It was so loud. She had not realised how loud guns were. The group disappeared round the corner and before she knew it, her mother had grabbed her hand and was pulling her and her sister away from the scene. There was a body on the ground, and she could see it was covered in blood. She felt sick, but found it difficult to look away.

'Don't look, Halina,' Eugenia said, her own face white and bloodless.

'Is he dead?' Halina managed to say.

'He's German,' she replied, as if that really mattered. The shock of seeing their first dead body took no account of nationality.

By the time they arrived home, Halina was shaking all over. It was only a dead German. It should not have affected her so much.

'Don't think about it,' she heard her mother say, 'just think that our gallant soldiers have started to repel the enemy.'

Halina sat in the kitchen and a feeling of faintness came over her. Her mother's voice seemed very far away. What was she saying? A cup of water appeared in her hand. Why did her hand keep shaking? She was splashing water everywhere. Ola did not seem very upset. Perhaps she had not seen the body. If she did not pull herself together, Ola would never let her hear the end of it.

Ola rushed into the kitchen saying there were Germans in the street. They looked out of the window and could see several motorbikes approaching noisily.

'Quick, into the cellar,' shouted Eugenia. She pulled back the carpet and opened the trap door, shooing her daughters down the wooden steps into the darkness below. The door shut with a bang behind them. They passed through another door into the main cellar and she locked the door. There was a narrow window at street level and they could see boots in the street outside, moving past the window. They stayed in the cellar for some time, until it seemed quiet outside. They climbed slowly back into the kitchen, holding their breath - scarcely breathing at all.

'I think they have gone,' said Eugenia eventually.

The next few days were spent in apprehension. Every time Halina heard a loud noise she jumped nervously, but the German soldiers were nowhere to be seen.

On Sunday the family went to Mass, thankful that the German soldiers had not been seen for several days. The church in Kamionka took on a special significance for Halina in the holidays, as this was where she would see Stefan. He was a student at Lwow University, but he came home at the holidays and would come to Mass with his parents, who were friendly with the Korbinskis.

When she sat down in the church Halina looked around, trying not to make it obvious that she was doing so. Her caution was rewarded. There, several rows in front, sat the object of her romantic fantasies. Halina stared at the back of his head. His hair curled round his ears in such a nice way. Perhaps he would turn his head so she would be able see his face. Ola dug her in the ribs, and she realised she should be kneeling. She quickly sank to her knees and bowed her head as she had been taught. Once everyone else was praying, she could open her eyes and watch Stefan. No one would notice.

After Mass, she stood next to her mother as she greeted friends and neighbours, and was delighted to see Stefan approaching with his parents. She must try to look casual as if she did not care whether he was there or not. But what if she started blushing? That would be so embarrassing. She looked across at Anita, Stefan's mother, and saw that she was smiling indulgently at her. Halina felt her mouth go dry. Stefan was so handsome; Anita must know that she admired him. How could she know what she was thinking? Halina's embarrassment was complete when Stefan winked at her. She walked home with her face burning. But by the time she arrived at the house she felt a little better. He had looked flattered after all.

Later that week an increasing number of strangers appeared in the street, carrying bags and cases. Some drove in cars or wagons, some came by train, some by foot, but all wore a haunted look. Eugenia spoke to one or two, directing them this way or that.

'They have come from the west,' she said to Halina, 'to escape the German army.'

'But there are Germans here.'

'Only a few and they were driven back by our soldiers. We saw that fight in the forest the other day. '

Halina stood outside the house fascinated by the activity in the street. As she watched, she became aware of a sense of desperation mirrored in the faces of those who passed. She turned to go back into the house when she noticed an old woman with a young boy who appeared to be her grandson. The couple were dressed in good quality clothes, but they were creased and dirty as if they had not been changed for days. The old woman sat down on a nearby bench and looked about her with an expression of bewilderment. The boy sat down beside her, clutching his small bag, his face grubby and tear-stained. Halina wondered vaguely where his mother was.

'Is it safe here?' the old woman asked, 'We have come to stay with my sister who lives here. But is it safe?' She turned her pale blue eyes on Halina, who was at a loss

14

what to say.

'Yes, I think so,' she replied, but the woman did not seem to hear her. She stood up stiffly, grasped her case in one hand and her grandson in the other and carried on along the street, stopping every now and then to put her case down.

'But is it safe?' Halina heard her asking over and over again. She watched the old woman as she walked away and felt very uneasy. It had seemed like fun at first to watch the strangers in the street, but they all looked so unhappy. And that poor little boy – he looked completely lost. What must it feel like to have to leave your house when you didn't want to? What if you had nowhere to go?

The next week was very quiet. The German soldiers seen a few weeks before had been few in number, but even they had disappeared. Initially it appeared that the Polish army had defeated them, but the radio gave no such news.

The answer came a few days later on September 17th when it was announced that the Soviets had entered eastern Poland. Everyone talked about it. Eugenia's friends assembled in her parlour soon after the news had been announced and they talked excitedly. 'The Germans have gone,' they exclaimed, 'The Soviets have come to our aid.'

Later that day, Halina was in her favourite position at a window looking over the river valley, when she saw soldiers walking along the main street. She rushed downstairs to look for her mother who was sitting reading a book.

'Mama, come quickly, there are soldiers in the town.'

'They must be Soviet soldiers,' Eugenia said, 'people are saying they have come to Poland's aid, but I am not so sure. Why have they really come?'

Halina stood behind the garden hedge watching the soldiers passing through. Her mother had forbidden her to leave the garden, but she could not resist watching the spectacle. First came a few cars, followed by several tanks, which appeared frighteningly large to her. The ground vibrated beneath her feet and she put her fingers in her ears. The noise they made was deafening. The tank hatches were open and she could see Soviet soldiers peering out of the top.

A small group of men on horseback came next, followed by line after line of soldiers. But these were not soldiers like those in her father's company - not soldiers with shining black boots and smart uniforms. They did not march proudly through, in perfect step, with rifles held stiffly upright. Their boots were covered in mud and some did not appear to have boots at all. The uniforms were equally dirty and some even had string round their waist instead of a belt. The group ambled along in an almost casual manner – they were never in step and their rifles were slung casually over their shoulders. What kind of army was this?

There were several Ukrainian families in the town and Halina saw one family she knew, standing on the street, cheering the soldiers and throwing flowers in their path. Everyone else she could see was watching in silence. Eventually, the last group of soldiers passed through the town and disappeared towards Lwow. Nothing was left but some crushed flower petals, and a faint vibration in the distance. Halina was confused. Obviously, the Ukrainians believed the Soviets had come to protect them, but she had heard so many stories from Papa about the defeat of the Soviets in 1920. Surely, they would not help Poland after being defeated by them less than twenty years before.

A few days later, the radio announced that Soviet Russia had in fact invaded Poland from the east. Poland had been invaded by two countries. However, people still could not quite believe it. The Soviets seen had mostly passed on through – there was no aggression, or had been thought.

Halina joined her mother as she listened to the radio later that day. The subject of politics was becoming more puzzling. She needed to try to make sense of things in case she was affected. Papa had not trusted the Soviets and she had to know what was happening. She sat in the parlour reading a book, listening to the radio with half an ear.

Suddenly her mother gasped, 'Oh no, not that.'

Halina looked up in alarm. 'What is it Mama?'

'Soviet Russia has made a treaty with Germany. They have divided Poland up. The west to Germany, the east to Soviet Russia.'

'But I don't understand. What do you mean?'

'The Soviets have claimed eastern Poland - we really have been invaded by them. We are all to become Soviets.'

Halina shifted uneasily in her seat. Papa had been right not to trust the Soviets. The Polish army had not defeated the Germans; they had drawn back. The invaders had agreed with Soviet Russia to allow them eastern Poland. But how would it affect her?

Eugenia's friend Dorota Milewska came to the door the next day in great distress. She was the wife of the mayor and usually heard news before anyone else. She stood in the hall crying. 'It is terrible,' she kept saying. Eventually, after some coaxing, Eugenia managed to get her to sit down and rest. 'It is terrible,' she repeated, 'as you know there were some soldiers left stationed in the barracks. They fought off those Germans that came here. But the Soviets we saw did not all pass through. There was a fight. There were only a few of our soldiers left and they were cut off from the rest of the army.'

'Of course, the rest of the army has gone towards Warsaw,' Eugenia interrupted, thinking of Kazimierz.

Dorota continued, 'Our soldiers were vastly outnumbered and they had to surrender. However, their commander could not do that. He just could not surrender to the Soviets, so he rode into the forest and committed suicide. It is just terrible. Our soldiers, left behind to defend us, were caught between two armies and unable to reach the rest of their company. Surrounded on all sides, some fought, some surrendered, and all were defeated. What will become of us now?'

16

FOUR

Eugenia at the piano. 'She would have to leave the piano she loved so much.'

Eugenia, Halina, Ola, October 1939, Kamionka Strumilowa

As the days progressed, more Soviets began to appear, this time to stay. This fact was underlined by the presence of wives, girlfriends and camp followers. Refugees were seen in the streets again. They had left their homes in western Poland to escape the Germans, some coming to stay with relatives nearby. Now they were trapped between two invaders and did not know what to do. Some had found their relatives, only to discover a few days later that the house had been commandeered, others to discover that their uncles, sons or brothers had been arrested or even shot. Some decided to try to go back to the west.

The atmosphere had changed in the town, although people tried to carry on as normal and the schools started as expected. The initial euphoria had died away quickly, and it soon became apparent that the situation was very grave.

With her children back at school, Eugenia felt at a loss. Before the war, she had spent her days meeting friends for lunch, preparing for dinner parties and balls, walking in the park, or fulfilling her important social role as an officer's wife in a small town.

Now there were no balls, no one could afford to have dinner parties and walking alone in the park might seem like an invitation to a lonely Soviet soldier. Perhaps she should go and see Dorota Milewska. The mayor's wife was a sweet soul, with few airs and graces. Besides, Tadeusz, her husband, had been very welcoming when they had first arrived in Kamionka.

As she approached Dorota's door she found it slightly ajar and from inside she heard the faint sounds of weeping.

'Dorota, are you there? It is Giena Korbinska.'

She pushed open the door and walked in to find her friend sitting on the settee weeping copiously.

'Dorota, my dear, what is the matter?' She touched Dorota on the arm and she jumped nervously.

'Oh Giena, Tadeusz has gone. He has been arrested.'

'Arrested! But why? Who has arrested him?'

'The Soviet police – the NKVD. They came this morning. Four of them. Four for my Tadeusz. They said he was an enemy of the people and whisked him away. I cannot see him. They will not let me see him. I do not know where he has gone or when he is coming back.....or if.'

Eugenia put her arms round her friend, 'Do not worry I am sure it is just a mistake.'

'I wish I could think that,' Dorota replied, 'but the husband of my friend Gabriela in Lwow, was arrested four weeks ago and has not been seen since.'

Eugenia left Dorota after an hour, and walked home with a feeling of dread in the pit of her stomach. She could not understand why they would arrest someone like Tadeusz. What had he done wrong? The world as she knew it was starting to crumble and the future was uncertain and frightening. She walked into the house without even registering that she had closed the door behind her, and sat on the stairs in the hall. She did not know if Kazimierz was free or captured, alive or dead, and the uncertainty was eating away at her. Why did he have to go? Eugenia pressed her temples in an attempt to ward off the headache that was threatening. Why did men have to go to war? They protected and controlled their women, then went off to fight, leaving them unprepared to deal with all these worries. Damn them! Damn them all!

Suddenly there was a loud knocking at the door, and she jumped up guiltily, half expecting to see Father Wolski on the step berating her for her unchristian thoughts. She was so relieved to see two soldiers there that she started to smile.

One of the soldiers spoke. 'We need this house for an officer and his family.'

Eugenia froze, and the smile died within her before it was born. 'But this is my house,' she managed to gasp, 'how can an officer and his family live here?'

'Madam,' the taller of the two advanced threateningly towards her, 'we need this house. You have until tomorrow evening to pack and leave.'

'But where will I go?' Eugenia grasped the banister to steady herself.

'That is not our problem. I repeat for the last time. We need this house. If you are not gone by tomorrow evening ....' The soldier did not finish his sentence, but took his gun from his shoulder and looked at her. The meaning was clear. Go or be shot. They turned and left, slamming the door loudly as they went.

Eugenia sat down again, panic rising in her. Where could she go? It was a lot to ask someone to take in her and the girls. Six months in Kamionka was a short time to build up a large circle of friends. Dorota would have taken them in, but now she had too many worries of her own. If only they were still in Lwow. They had many friends there, but Dorota's tales of arrest in Lwow were worrying. Eugenia sighed. It would have to be the Mirons. They were good friends, but how close can a friend of only six months become? An evening social function was one thing, but living all day, every day with Veronica Miron was another. She stood up unsteadily. It was no good having doubts. She had no choice. She would have to throw herself on the Mirons' mercy.

As Eugenia walked the half mile to Veronica's house, she wrestled with the practical problems of moving. She would have to decide what to take with her and what to leave. At least the frequent moving around with Kazimierz meant that she had packing cases as well as suitcases. She was well used to packing, and on the way back she would call in on Old Ryszard, who often provided transport for the army wives. He would have a van or at least a horse and cart to transport them. The girls! She stopped walking for a minute. She would have to meet them from school and tell them. She did not want them to find out from someone else.

Two hours later Eugenia sat once more on the stairs in the hall. Veronica had hugged her tightly and said she would be only too glad to help out. 'Stay as long as you need,' she had said. Old Ryszard had promised a van, one of the few he had left not commandeered by the Soviets. 'Better use it while I still have it, I expect the Soviets to take it any day,' he had said, shaking his head in disgust.

Eugenia looked at the clock in the hall. Two pm - that meant she had an hour to work out what she could take before she had to go and meet the girls. As she stood up, she felt very faint and remembered she had not had any lunch, but the thought of food made her feel sick, and besides, there was no time to eat. She would make up for it in the evening.

She walked into the living room and the first thing she saw was her piano. Suddenly the enormity of the day's events hit home. She sat on the stool and touched the smooth rosewood surface of the piano, scarcely noticing that her hand was trembling. She would have to leave the piano she loved so much. A wedding present from her parents, it had travelled all round eastern Poland with her, each time Kazimierz had a new posting. There would be no time to sell it, even if she could find a buyer. She moved over to the cabinets in the dining room. The glass and the china – she could take some of that perhaps, but she could not take the furniture.

Eugenia moved from room to room, touching an ornament here, a book there, panic building at each step. She would have to leave nearly everything. Everything she had built up over sixteen years of marriage. For a moment, her feelings threatened to overwhelm her, and silent tears rolled down her cheeks. Then the hall clock chimed three. She could not think about it now. She sat on the stairs one last time, taking deep breaths, willing her heart to slow and her tears to stop. She had to go and meet the girls. She had to find the words to tell them.

Halina was surprised to see her mother waiting outside her school, even more so when she saw that Ola was in tow. She said goodbye to her friends and walked over towards Eugenia. 'Why are you here, Mama? Is something wrong?'

Eugenia drew a breath. She had not yet told Ola the reason for her presence, but she could put it off no longer. 'I wanted to make sure you hurried home,' she said, trying to smile but not quite succeeding, 'we are going to stay with the Mirons for a bit and will have to start packing tonight.'

'Oh, I see.' Halina looked puzzled. 'Do you want some company now that Papa has gone? How long will we be there?'

'We will have to stay, girls,' she glanced at Ola, who looked ready to cry, 'The Soviets are taking over the house. We have to be out by tomorrow.' Now she had said it. She held her breath for a moment.

Halina stopped mid-stride. 'Taken our house! How can they take our house. How can you let them take our house!'

'Halina, ssh, you are shouting, you will frighten Ola,' Eugenia looked around to see who had heard.

'I'm not afraid,' Ola chimed in, 'just deafened,' and she glowered at Halina.

Eugenia started walking in the direction of home, 'We have no choice girls. If we do not, they might….might.' She faltered.

'I don't care if they shoot us,' continued Halina, somehow guessing what her mother might say.

Eugenia glanced at Ola again, who really was starting to look frightened.

'No one is shooting anyone,' she said, sounding more confident than she felt, 'But we must be ready to go tomorrow.'

Halina grunted but said nothing more. She would not let those Soviets get the better of her. How dare they steal her house! She would get her revenge one day.

The sun was beginning to set behind the hills surrounding the town, as later that day Eugenia sat in the garden with a glass of wine. It would probably be her last, as she could no longer spare money for such luxuries. The small poetry book on her lap was forgotten as she leaned against the wall and tried to rid her mind of the worries that had invaded it. What would the future hold for her and the girls? What would they lose next? Would she see Kazimierz again? He was so patriotic, so intensely patriotic. He would be devastated at the changes taking place in his country. Now they were about to lose nearly everything that they had shared together. Everything except for the children. Thank God she had the children.

Eugenia no longer tried to stop the tears from flowing. All that day she had held them back as she tried to remain cheerful for the sake of Halina and Ola. Now that her daughters were in bed, her carefully built defences dissolved. She leaned forward and wept, hardly noticing that the poetry book had fallen off her lap and knocked over her glass of wine. The blood red contents trickled over the ground and soaked into the cool Polish earth.

Halina woke with a strange feeling of dread. It took her several moments to come to and remember why she was feeling as she did. Today they would have to pack everything they could and leave their house, a house to which they could never return.

Breakfast was a hurried affair, and soon she was sitting in her room surrounded by her possessions. Mama had said she could only use one large suitcase and part of a packing case. The Mirons did not have room for more. That would mean she could not take everything. She was used to packing, as the family moved every few years when her father had new postings, but this time was different. How could she decide what to leave? She wandered round her bedroom. She could take most of her clothes, but there would be no room for books. She picked up an ancient teddy bear perched on the dressing table. She was far too old for bears now, so she would have to put him out to pasture.

She started packing as she had done many times in the past, but for some reason her hands were shaking, and every now and then her eyes prickled and her nose ran. What would happen to the things she left? Would those dreadful Soviets get them? She collected the chess set and some ornaments and crammed then in a bag with the bear. They would go out with the rubbish. If she could not have them, there was no way she would leave them for some Soviet girl to abuse. She folded up her bed linen, ready to put in the packing case, but the bed cover, the curtains and her favourite bedside rug were too bulky to take. Mama had said she would let Old Ryszard take them. At least they would be in a Polish home.

She sat on the case and fastened the clasps. That was that. There was no point in crying now. She could not take anything else, and she could do nothing about it.

Later, Halina sat on the stairs looking at the pile of cases and chests in the hall. She stood up and wandered into her father's study, touching the things of his that they had been unable to pack. On his desk was a small silver snuffbox, tarnished from recent lack of care. She picked it up and opened it. It looked very like Edmund's tinderbox. She took the flint that she still carried about with her wrapped in cloth, and put it in the box. It fitted perfectly, still leaving room for the family photographs she had decided to take.

There was a photo of Mama playing the piano, one of Papa in his uniform, looking severe, and several of her with Ola. She picked up one of Mama, looking beautiful and wearing a large hat. A very young Halina was perched on her knee and her father was looking over her mother's shoulder with a cheeky expression on his face. They both looked so young and carefree. She put the box in her pocket. She needed something of Papa's. After all, he really had looked sad when he said goodbye to her

Old Ryszard arrived with his van and piled the luggage in the back. As they drove along the tree-lined path beside the river, Halina watched her house shrinking into the distance. She had not left just curtains and carpets. She had left part of her heart behind as well.

FIVE

Halina in school uniform.
'When she returned home with Ola in tow,
Halina showed Eugenia the leaflet.'

Eugenia, Halina, Ola, November 1939, Kamionka Strumilowa

Halina looked at her history essay. It had not been marked. She knew there was a mistake in it. She had remembered the correct dates after she had handed it in, and had been afraid it might lower her marks. But her teacher had not noticed the mistake. In fact, the only sign she had looked at it at all, was the word 'Good' written at the end. What was the point of all that work if the teacher did not mark it properly? And that was not all that was strange. She had talked with Adela all through maths, expecting to be told off, but nothing happened. Miss Wilk had said nothing. And she was usually so fierce. What was going on? She put away the essay and brought out her notebook. At least it was Father Wojtek now.

The priest was a great favourite with her friends. He was in his late twenties and very handsome, so all her friends were in love with him. The fact that he was a priest and thus unattainable, only increased his attraction, and everyone vied for his attention. Natalia and Klara even had competitions to see who could make him blush more. She nudged Adela as the door opened. Their favourite lesson was about to begin.

However, it was not Father Wojtek. It was someone else altogether. Adela whispered that it was the leader of the local communist party. Someone normally ignored. Why was he here? 'Where is Father Wojtek?' Halina asked.

'He is no longer here,' was the reply.

And that was it. No explanation. Where had he gone? There was a rumour that the NKVD had arrested the headmaster, but she had not believed it. Perhaps it was true after all. As the lesson progressed, she sat with her pen poised over her book, amazed at what she was being told. The new teacher was telling them about the glorious Russian revolution and about the great leader Stalin. She looked at Adela who was pulling a face. Where they supposed to learn this rubbish? At the end of the lesson, leaflets were handed out. Halina was about to crumple up her copy, when she noticed the last few sentences. The leaflet was encouraging them to rise against their enemies. Not the Germans or Soviets it seemed, but the leaders and landowners. The sentence that caught her eye was the one that included the 'officer class' amongst the enemies of the people.

'Enemies of the people! What kind of rubbish is that,' she said to Adela, 'How can we be enemies of the people?'

Ola picked up her school case and followed Halina. It was just so annoying that she had to walk home from school with Halina and her friends. It was not even as if she was going to her own house. The Mirons house was much closer, but she had no choice. Mama had forbidden her from walking home alone, and she had to wait around until Halina came to collect her, before she could leave school.

'We just do not know what those Soviet soldiers will do,' Mama had said, 'you must not come home alone.'

And so here she was trailing along behind, while Halina and her friends talked about all sorts of boring things. She rubbed her scalp, which still smarted a little after Sabina Milewska had pulled her pigtails. Sabina had been happy to be her friend as long as she thought she was the prettiest in the class and Ola just the cleverest. But today she had overheard several girls saying that they thought Ola was the prettiest as well as the cleverest. Ola rubbed her scalp again and smiled. A warm glow of triumph kept her company the rest of the way home.

When she returned home with Ola in tow, Halina showed Eugenia the leaflet. 'Look at this, Mama,' she said, 'look at the rubbish they are giving us now.'

She was surprised to see that her mother appeared to take it very seriously.

'The Mirons will not like this,' she said. 'As it is, I think we are rather a burden, and letters like this will only make them think that they might become targets.'

After the evening meal, Halina took her schoolbooks from the room she shared with Adela, and went outside to sit in the garden. The Mirons had been very quiet throughout dinner and even Adela seemed to have been affected by the leaflet. It was all very odd. When she had first started at her school in Kamionka, she had immediately made friends with Adela and several other girls. Her father was an officer and officers were members of the social and intellectual elite – a fact that was widely recognised.

Things were very different now. She was a guest in Adela's house – only there because she had nowhere else to go - and the roles had shifted dramatically. Now Adela put on airs and seemed to be trying her best to put her in her place when she could. Surely she did not believe what was written in the leaflet? Halina shook her head. Since the leaflet citing officers as 'enemies of the people' had appeared, the atmosphere in the Miron house had become distinctly unfriendly.

December 1939

'Nothing! You mean we have no money at all?' Eugenia suddenly felt very weak and spots seemed to swarm in front of her.

'There now Mrs Korbinska, do not worry.' Andrzej Wilgut rose from his desk, reached out a plump, white hand and poured some water into a glass. He walked round his desk and stood nervously next to Eugenia, his hand shaking slightly as he passed her the water.

'How can I not worry if I have no money! Where has it gone? How can it have gone? We are well off. We have a great deal of money!'

'It is the Soviets,' replied Andrzej, retreating to safety on his side of the desk, 'they reduced the zloty to a fraction of its original value, as you know when you came to change the zloty your husband left you, and just this week, they abolished it altogether. We must pay for everything in roubles now. It is not just you my dear Mrs Korbinska; everyone is in the same boat. Everyone.'

'But what will I do?' Eugenia felt some colour return to her face, but Mr Wilgut seemed far away.

'You must sell things,' replied the banker, feeling a little more comfortable now he could offer advice, 'sell things. The Soviets have money, especially the NKVD, but they have nothing to spend it on in Russia. They think Poland is like fairyland and they rush to buy anything, anything at all. A good pair of second hand shoes will sell for at least 500 roubles. That will keep you in food for several weeks.'

Eugenia struggled to come to terms with the news. 'But how can I sell them? Where do I go – to the market?'

'Yes, my dear. Set up a stall and the customers will come flocking.'

Eugenia walked out of the bank, still a little shaky. She would have to sell things. In the market. Like a common trader.

Later that morning, Eugenia stood against the wall in the Miron's kitchen feeling the cool surface against her back. There was only some cheese and a few potatoes left in the larder, and she would have to replace what the Mirons had given her. She still had money from Kazimierz, but she did not know how long it would have to last, and now her savings were gone.

Faintly through the wall she heard Adela and Halina arguing, but in a reasonably good-natured way. She smiled briefly at the girlish voices and found the sound calmed her a little. She pushed herself off the wall, picked up her basket and stuffed in her red shoes. Those shoes had last been turning and twisting round the dance floor at the final ball before Kazimierz left. Now they would be used to buy food.

'Just going to the market for some food, girls,' she shouted, 'I won't be long.' A faint reply drifted past as she shut the door behind her and walked resolutely down the street.

As she came nearer to the market, Eugenia found her footsteps slowing. Could she really do this? She was an officer's wife. She was used to having a maid and many fine things. Here she was, reduced to selling things for food. Although the word selling was what she said to herself, somehow it changed to begging by the time she heard it. A flush of shame began to steal its way across her cheeks. She looked around nervously, but could see no one she knew. What would people think of her? As she turned the corner she stopped suddenly, overcome with embarrassment. There in front of her was Anna Wilgut, the banker's wife. Only a few short months ago when Kazimierz was at home, Anna had sat at her dinner table drinking wine from crystal glasses and eating nine courses from the best china. How could she face her now?

She started to change direction so that she could creep away without being seen, but it was too late, Anna was upon her.

'Eugenia!' she said, 'How are you my dear. Have you come to sell something? It takes a bit of getting used to I know, but Andrzej says everyone is doing it. Must go, I hear the butcher has some nice pork.' With that, she scurried towards the market, her short, plump legs wobbling as she went.

That brief encounter left Eugenia feeling a little less ashamed. If everyone was doing it…. As she approached the market square, she was astonished at the number of people around. As she surveyed the scene, she saw familiar faces at every turn. There was the schoolteacher's wife selling some clothes. Was that not the mayor's daughter with some bed linen?

She stood awkwardly with her red shoes in her hand, wondering what to do next, when a face appeared at her elbow.

'What you want?'

Eugenia turned and saw a young Soviet woman standing next to her looking eagerly at her.

'What you want?'

Eugenia realised the stuttering Polish was aimed at her. '600 roubles,' she replied in Russian. 'These are very high quality shoes from Warsaw. A bargain at the price.'

She expected some protest at the sum, which was double what the shoes were worth, but there was none. The woman grabbed the shoes and stuffed the money into Eugenia's hand, without even trying on the shoes. She stood in disbelief looking at the money. It was so easy! That money would last for weeks, and that was just one pair of shoes. Relief flooded over her. The future suddenly seemed a little less dark.

SIX

Eugenia, Halina, Ola, December 1939, Kamionka Strumilowa

'They cannot stay any longer.' Staszek Miron became increasingly red in the face as he warmed to his subject. 'It is just too much of a risk. It was bad enough when our savings vanished two weeks ago and we still had to support them, but now it seems they are a target because they are an officer's family. I heard in the post office that some people in uniform have been asking which houses the army officers lived in. Why would anyone want to know that? The Soviets have taken over their house, and they might find evidence that an army officer's family lived there and come looking for them here.'

'But they are our friends,' protested Veronica to her husband.

'Friends do not bring danger,' he replied, 'you must tell them to go.'

Eugenia entered the room where the couple were arguing and they stopped open-mouthed, as they realised she had heard everything said.

'I will leave the day after tomorrow,' she said.

'Eugenia it is fine, he does not mean it,' Veronica looked from Eugenia to her husband and back again, 'really.'

'I think he does,' Eugenia replied as she turned and left the room. She had been dreading this moment, but at least Staszek had finally said what he had been thinking for some time. Now she would have to tell the girls they were moving again. She swallowed hard - the lump in her throat was making it difficult to breath.

On Halina's return from school that day, she found her mother surrounded by piles of clothes and linen, her jewel box on the table beside her.

'We must go to Luck to stay with your Aunt Zosia,' she announced, 'The Miron's do not want us to stay any longer. We are an officer's family and they have heard that people are being arrested. If we go to Luck we will not be known and we might be safer.'

'Mama, what do you mean,' she asked, 'why are we not safe?'

Eugenia looked at her, but could not bring herself to say anything that might upset her daughter. 'Halina,' she said, 'we do not want to bring any danger to them. We must leave.'

'Are you packing everything?' Halina asked, looking round at the piles of clothes.

'I will sell what I can,' she said, 'I have found it easy in the past, but I am not sure how such a large quantity will sell.'

The next day Halina watched in dismay as her beautiful, elegant, mother walked to the market pushing a cart loaded with her best clothes and jewels, as if she were a common street trader. Most of her mother's ball gowns were squashed in the back along with old toys and her father's suits. She knew how much her mother loved those dresses, but if she regretted letting them go she did not say. 'We will need money,' was all she would say

27

Halina had been vaguely aware that food from the market appeared at the same time that some clothes disappeared, but she had not realised until now just what her mother had to go through to put food on the table. She felt a little ashamed that she had eaten the food, even complaining occasionally about its monotony, without recognising how it got there. Mama was getting thinner, and she looked very pale at times. She also had a few grey threads in her hair. Perhaps it was time she thought more about her mother and less about herself.

Eugenia set the clothes out on the table she had brought with her in the cart. In the last few weeks, she had only sold a pair of shoes and two sweaters, preferring to barter with the shopkeepers than to interact with the Soviet girls. Those were the people who had thrown her out of her house, and who had arrested people she counted as her friends. They had stolen virtually all of her money and had turned her life upside down. Yet she needed money and had to pretend to be polite to those scruffy, ignorant women whom she despised. She could not bear the thought of them wearing her dresses, of her jewellery touching their skin, of her sheets being soiled by their sexual encounters.

Everything she saw had memories attached that made her task even more difficult. That navy dress with the daring red slashes was the one she wore to the opera house, before they left Lwow two years ago. That blue dress was the one she wore to her younger sister Barbara's wedding, and those crystal glasses were given to her by Kazimierz' mother when they last visited her in her grand house in Warsaw.

'I do not need all this now,' she had said, pressing china and glasses on Eugenia. 'Now that Kazimierz' father is dead I do not entertain. I have let out the other two floors and am content to live simply now. I have given much to Kazimierz' cousin Janina - she wants to impress prospective customers of her school – but I wanted you to have these.' Eugenia wondered what Grandma Korbinska would think of her selling her gifts. She would probably understand. She understood so much.

Saturday was the main market day and there were a large number of stalls around her. However, the fact that others she knew were in the same situation, served only to intensify her feelings of disgust. This time she would not speak politely in Russian, this time it would be Polish or nothing. As a potential customer approached, it took all of her concentration not to spit in the girl's face. She conjured up an image of a pale Ola, left to starve because her mother was too proud, and just managed to paste a smile on her face.

The first customer had obviously just arrived from Russia. Her hair was short and looked as if she had cut it herself without using a mirror. Her eyebrows were thick and dark and met in the middle. She had attempted to make herself up, but the powder did little to hide the broken veins on her face, and her teeth were smeared with lipstick. She picked up Eugenia's favourite red and navy dress, holding it up to herself, back to front. The red clashed horribly with her lipstick and the navy enhanced the lankness of her hair. Eugenia looked on in amazement as the girl chatted excitedly to her friend. Did she not realise the dress was back to front? She decided to say nothing.

The girl tucked the dress under her arm and picked up a nursing bra. Eugenia had thought that no one would want such an item, but decided that as she had hardly used the bra, she might as well bring it. The girl looked at the bra in confusion. She turned it round and commented to her friend that the Polish had large ears. Despite the situation, Eugenia had to stop herself laughing aloud. The woman thought it was a pair of earmuffs! She looked across to the schoolteacher's wife who was selling at a table next to her. She had seen the incident and mouthed 'stupid' at her. Eugenia felt a little better, but the incident did nothing to stop the coldness of the day creeping into her heart.

As the morning wore on, Eugenia regretted her decision to speak Polish only. The Soviet girls did not realise she could understand them when they discussed the items she had to sell. On the other hand, perhaps they did not care if she understood them. She was nothing. Just some Polish person to speak in front of as one would a small child. The Soviet girls kept coming, excitedly buying everything in sight. As the piles on the table reduced in size, she felt more and more depressed. Each sale drove home the same message over and over. Her life as she knew it had gone and might never return.

Eugenia returned home several hours later with only a handful of items, determined not to let her children know how difficult she had found the experience.

'It is unbelievable,' she said, affecting enthusiasm, 'There were Soviet women there who had never seen a ball gown. They just pounced on everything. I cannot believe how quickly things sold. Nearly everything I took. As for my jewellery, I only took a few of the poorer items, but they treated them as if they were the best diamonds.'

She sat down and looked around her. 'We have cases enough for what is left. I do not want to sell it all at once. It might become useful. Halina you must pack everything of yours that is left. I have train tickets. We are going to Luck tomorrow.'

The next morning Eugenia rose very early. She had arranged for Old Ryszard to take their cases to the station. Apart from the fact that he had driven for her before on many occasions, and she knew he could be trusted, his cousin, Young Ryszard, worked at Luck station and had been able to get train tickets for them. She explained to Halina a few hours later when they were ready to leave, 'Mr and Mrs Miron had offered to take us to the station, but it is a gesture of guilt, I think. Besides, I know they are having trouble getting hold of fuel for their car.'

She had debated for some time whether it would be safer to travel to Luck by train or cart. She realised that they would be rather conspicuous getting on a train with several cases and more likely to be arrested. Yet, if they travelled to Luck in a cart with the cases, it would be obvious they were running away and it would arouse suspicion, should they encounter any Soviet soldiers.

In the end, the solution was that Old Ryszard would load the cases on the train and travel in another carriage from them. At their destination, Young Ryszard would meet him and help him unload and then take the cases to her sister's house. The sight of an old man in rough clothing unloading cases would not attract any interest, as it was a common sight these days. The families of the Soviet soldiers were arriving daily, and porters were in great demand. His cousin had already taken a message to her sister Zosia in Luck, so she would be expecting her.

When they were ready to leave, they swept out of the house with barely a backward glance. The Mirons were standing nervously on the doorstep, but Eugenia had already thanked them for their hospitality, albeit with some sarcasm in her tone, and she did not want to pretend she was sorry to leave. She grasped Ola's hand very tightly as they walked the few hundred yards to the station with Halina following behind. Unknown to her, Halina had turned round and was making rude gestures at Adela for her betrayal.

Eugenia was very nervous at the station as they waited for the train. She walked up and down, looking around the station for signs of Soviets who might stop them. However, there was no one except Old Ryszard. He seemed to know what she was worried about and said, 'I expect they're sleeping off the vodka they drank last night. Don't worry now, you will be fine.'

When the train arrived, he loaded their cases and made sure they found their seats. 'Good luck. And you girls look after your mother.'

The train whistled and Eugenia realised he had gone. Gone too was her comfortable, privileged life. If only she was not worrying so much about what was going to replace it.

Seven

Halina. 'Perhaps she would get the chance to be a Polish heroine some day.'

Eugenia, Halina, Ola, December 1939, Luck

Once they were on the train, Halina noticed that her mother had relaxed a little. They had a carriage with no corridor, so as long as the train was moving they would be safe. The first snows of winter had arrived and the surrounding countryside was clean and white, with the green conifers wearing white caps. Ola was drawing pictures and colouring them in with her precious pencils, but Halina sat and studied her mother who was looking out of the window at the passing countryside. She looked very sad, signs of tension mirrored in the frequency with which she pushed her hair from her face and smoothed her skirt. Halina caught her eye and for a moment saw some deep sadness within, but it was quickly covered with a bright smile.

'Not long now,' she said. Halina smiled weakly in reply. She was not convinced by the pretence that all was well.

The train stopped at a station and Eugenia stiffened again, looking out of the window for signs of Soviet uniforms, but the only passenger waiting was an old woman with a goat, who ambled by and climbed into the goods wagon.

The train moved off again and Halina returned to her thoughts. Everything was so uncertain and she felt insecure and threatened, yet at the same time, a thread of excitement wove its way through her thoughts. Perhaps she would get the chance to be a Polish heroine some day.

She had travelled before to Luck to visit her mother's family, but always under happy circumstances and usually with her father. She looked at her mother again. She still seemed very anxious. The journey was taking such a long time. Normally the journey took several hours, but they had been travelling for half the day or so it seemed. Perhaps it was the snow, perhaps just her impatience.

The train stopped again and Eugenia leaned forward in her seat. Someone in Soviet uniform had boarded the train. 'It looks like NKVD,' she said. 'What do you think Halina?'

The soldier in question was alone and Halina noticed he was carrying a parcel in coloured paper. 'He is on his own,' she said, 'and is not paying much attention to anyone. It looks like he is off duty. Perhaps he is going to visit his girl friend.'

'You are quite the detective,' smiled Eugenia, and she relaxed again.

After several more hours, the train arrived at Luck station. By the time they had gathered themselves and their belongings together, and left the train, their luggage was sitting in a forlorn pile on the station platform. Old Ryszard and his cousin had decided to wait until the family had left before transporting the bags. They walked past the bags pretending not to notice them and walked the half mile from the station to Zosia's house.

'I am so glad you are here,' she said, when they arrived at her door, 'I have been so worried about you. I have got some food ready for you, although I was not sure when you would arrive.' Zosia was quite a few years older than Eugenia. Whereas Eugenia was tall and slim with dark eyes and hair, Zosia was small, fair and very plump. She had always doted on Eugenia, and never resented her beauty. Her husband had died several years after retiring from a period as the town mayor, and her younger daughter Agnieszka, had recently married and was living near Warsaw, close to her elder daughter. She had sold up her grand house in the centre of town when Agnieszka had married, and now lived in a quiet back street in a house built of warm golden brick with a red wooden front door.

She shepherded Eugenia and the girls to the table where she had laid out a meal. It was so good to see her sister and her nieces again. She had many friends in the town, but in the evenings, she always returned to a house that seemed empty without her daughters. She was glad of the company, especially in view of the recent invasion by the Soviets.

As her visitors ate, she thought of her own daughters. Agnieszka had been visiting her when the war started, and she had made the decision that she should return to Warsaw immediately. Zosia sighed. She regretted that decision every day, and worried constantly about the fate of her two daughters. Since the Soviet invasion, communication with Warsaw had become almost impossible.

Once everyone had eaten, she motioned Eugenia to sit by the fire. Ola went off to bed, but to her surprise, her sister insisted that Halina should stay. Still, it was not her place to decide what was suitable for Eugenia's daughter.

'It is not good here, Eugenia,' Zosia sighed, 'several people I know have disappeared so I don't know if they have just left or if they have been arrested. The Soviets are everywhere. They have taken over the finer houses in the town. The Buczacs have been pushed into one room and all their possessions taken over by a Soviet officer and his wife.'

Eugenia interrupted. 'Who are they arresting,' she asked, 'and what for?'

'I don't know. The Soviet police, the NKVD, wear soldier's uniforms, or at least I can't tell them apart. Some people say they are working with collaborators, Ukrainians mainly it seems, and are gathering information about everyone, or at least everyone who matters.'

'But who is being arrested?' she asked again.

'They are asking about everyone of importance in the town - business owners, bankers, teachers, and army officer's wives. The Soviets seem to think the intelligentsia could be a threat to them. It is not really safe here either,' she added, 'but at least you are not known. You will have to be very careful not to go out too much and must try not to be noticed.'

The news worried Eugenia. She had come to Luck thinking that they could move about in a larger town without people noticing them, but that now seemed less likely. However, she resolved, they would try to live as normal a life as possible, although Ola and Halina no longer had school, and their movements outside were to be somewhat restricted. Zosia had agreed that it would not be wise for two young girls to be out on their own with the Soviet soldiers around. 'At the very least they might ask why they are not in school,' said Zosia.

'Is school still on?' Halina asked.

'After a fashion,' Zosia replied, grimacing. 'One of my friends has two young daughters at school. She told me that several of the teachers were told to leave. Several others, including the headmaster just disappeared. We think they must have been arrested. There are several new teachers in the school teaching Soviet ideals.'

'Oh yes,' Halina interrupted, 'They had just started that at my school before I left.'

'But not only that,' continued Zosia, 'recently they have started talking against the church.'

Eugenia looked at her in horror. 'But they cannot do that. Surely the local priest will not let it happen.'

'Father Pienta was arrested several weeks ago. He has now disappeared.' Zosia continued, 'The lessons have changed, especially history. All they hear about is the Russian revolution and the life history of Stalin. It is dreadful. What will become of our children?' At this she felt as if she was about to cry, but managed to hold back her tears. 'Anyway, Giena my dear, it is so wonderful to have you here. But you must be careful.'

Eight

The destruction.
'One furniture store was completely empty and all the fittings removed.' (ILLUSTRATIVE IMAGE)

Eugenia, Halina, Ola, December 1939, Luck

Winter had come early that year, and it was becoming colder and colder. The snow was deeper than usual and every day the temperature was well below zero. The main streets were cleared of snow, but Zosia's little back street had a thick layer on the roads. There was no desire to clear the streets to make things easier for the Soviets. Because it was so cold, there was less incentive for Ola and Halina to go outside, especially as their usual noisy snowball fights had been banned, in case they drew unwelcome attention.

Halina sat looking out of the window trying to ignore how bored she felt. They had only been in Luck for two weeks and already she felt confined. Much of what Aunt Zosia and Mama discussed left her unaffected. She had never owned anything of value, so did not appreciate the pain of those who had lost what they had spent years in creating.

The biggest problem that she had was boredom. She was not at school, was separated from her friends and was restricted with what she could do to entertain herself. Mama did her best to occupy her with some lessons on history and other subjects, and that helped a little, but there was nothing to use up her energy. Still, she had enjoyed the cooking lessons given to her earlier in the day by her aunt, who had promised to bring out her workbox after lunch. That would be fun. Aunt Zosia was very creative, and was expert in sewing, embroidery and crochet.

After lunch, Halina sat picking over a huge box full of coloured embroidery threads. She looked through the transfers and intricate designs with a sense of relief. Now she had something worthwhile to occupy her time. She would embroider handkerchiefs for Mama and her aunt, and just for a challenge, would choose a completely different range of shades from those shown in the coloured pattern books. She had never crocheted before, and Aunt Zosia had showed her how, and given her a box of wool to use. When Ola was in bed in the evenings, she would crochet a scarf for her. At least making Christmas presents for the next few weeks would keep her occupied.

Ola opened her notebook. Thank goodness Auntie Zosia had some in her cupboard. She had filled her last notebook and they did not seem to sell good quality paper in Luck. She opened the bag that held her drawing pencils. All this moving about was such a nuisance. At least Halina was with Auntie Zosia and she had the window seat to herself.

She looked out at the snowy street below. There were some soldiers in the street talking to a man in a light-coloured jacket. The man was sitting on the ground leaning against a lamppost. It was snowing again, which was a bit annoying as snow was so difficult to draw. If she had black paper and a white pencil, it would be much easier. She sighed. She would just have to try to make it work. What was it Papa had said? Something about problems making people creative? She picked up a black pencil. Well she was creative all the time.

She sketched the scene outside, trying hard to compose it well, as she had been taught in art. She sighed again. The soldiers were waving their arms about and making it difficult for her to draw them. One of the soldiers took the gun off his shoulder and started waving that. If only they would keep still. There was a muffled sound and then the soldiers moved off. The man was still there sitting against the lamppost.

Ola picked up her red pencil. A nice splash of colour. That would improve the picture a great deal. She had not noticed before that the man was wearing a red jacket. Funny that he should still be sitting there. It was very cold outside. Perhaps she should tell Mama. She put her pencil down and noticed that the man had fallen onto his side. Suddenly she remembered the dead German soldier in Kamionka. Mama thought she hadn't seen the body, but she had. She had forgotten about it until now. She tore the page out of her notebook and put it on the fire. She didn't want to think about it. She just hoped the man would not be there next time she went out.

As Christmas was coming, Halina and Eugenia took a trip to the centre of the town to look for Christmas presents.

'Nothing much,' Eugenia said before they left, 'just something to cheer us up – perhaps a few sweets. And I want a fur hat for Ola for Christmas.'

They left as soon as it was light and before the Soviet NKVD or their women were out of bed. There were many beautiful shops in the town, usually decorated in grand style for Christmas. This year however, there were almost no decorations. One of the best stores was renowned for its winter wear and this was where they went to look for Ola's fur hat, only to find that the shop was deserted, and the shelves almost bare. The owner, a round man in his sixties, was sitting in a corner. He jumped up when they came in. He looked around furtively. 'So nice to see some friendly faces,' he said.

'It looks like business is good,' said Eugenia, as she asked to see children's hats, 'I suppose the cold weather is the reason?'

The owner laughed bitterly. 'If only that were true. The Soviets have taken all the best items. The soldiers and their women come breezing in offering their roubles and expecting things for a fraction of the price. We had an NKVD official in the other day, and when I refused to accept what he offered for a coat, he just took it and said that I was lucky he did not shoot me! He did leave his money on the desk though, for what it was worth.'

'But you had so much stock last time we came,' said Eugenia.

'That is true,' he replied, smoothing his moustache in pride, 'We were renowned for being one of the best stores in the region. But these Soviets,' he looked round again and made a rude sign, 'they have never seen such things in their own shops. They seem to think this is fairyland or something. The women are the worst. They come in like locusts and sweep off just about everything that takes their fancy. And such excitement. You would think everything was gold plated.' He drew a breath, 'But I do have some children's hats tucked away,' and he drew out several fur hats from a drawer under the counter. The price he asked was so low Eugenia could not believe it, but she paid up and left quickly, before he changed his mind.

Many of the other shops seemed similarly depleted. One furniture store was completely empty and all the fittings removed. 'Shipped off to Russia,' said a woman passing by, who saw them standing and looking at the shop. 'And the factory that made the furniture. All of the machines stripped out and taken. Some of the skilled workers were taken as well.'

They found a shop that made its own sweets and chose a selection for Zosia as the owner described how difficult it was becoming to get supplies of sugar. Eugenia wished she had not come out. She had felt much more cheerful now that she was with Zosia, but everything had changed so much from her last visit, she hardly recognised the town. Luck was no longer the wealthy, bustling town it used to be. Now it looked like a poor peasant village from the past with no escape from the unpleasant facts of the present. Yet another reminder of how much her country had been damaged.

Zosia glanced at her sister sitting by the fire. She looked so sad these days. Whenever she had visited with Kazimierz and the children in the past, she had been happy and smiling. So full of life. Now the light within her had dimmed and when she smiled, it did not reach her eyes. She put on a good act for the children, but she knew her sister, and this was a stranger. She shifted the embroidery on her lap. At least Halina and Ola had adapted reasonably well, but then they did not understand all that Eugenia had to worry about. Zosia put down her embroidery. She would make sure Eugenia and the girls had a good Christmas. She would have to do some planning and talk to a few friends. She only had a few days left.

It proved difficult to obtain the usual Christmas fare, but Zosia managed to obtain a pike from a fisherman she knew, although she would have preferred the more traditional carp. When Eugenia was in bed, she prepared clear beetroot soup, and her friends offered to bring cranberry pudding and poppy seed dessert. She was ready.

Christmas Eve arrived and Eugenia, who had been expecting very little for Christmas, was pleasantly surprised when Zosia told her that they would have a traditional

Christmas Eve supper. She had been dreading a Christmas without Kazimierz and was glad there would be some activity to stop her brooding. It would be nice to have a reason for dressing up a little in the few decent clothes she had left.

When Zosia's friends arrived, it almost felt like it used to – dressing up, meeting new people, drinking a little, talking a little. However, when they moved to the table and started the meal with the traditional exchange of greetings and the division of wafer bread, Eugenia had to fight hard to hold back the tears. Kazimierz should be here. What was he doing? Was he in a prison somewhere? Was he dead? She looked round the table and saw that everyone was close to tears. Everyone was missing someone. But this was Christmas. Her sister had worked so hard to prepare the dinner for her. She had to look cheerful and try to be happy.

They sat down again, and her mood lifted a little as Zosia lit the candles on the small tree in the corner. She was used to thirteen or fourteen courses on Christmas Eve, but the three courses Zosia had provided meant so much more to her. She smiled at Zosia and squeezed her hand. It was wonderful to have someone to care for her again. A little of the tension of the last few months left her, and finally she started to enjoy the evening. She was not alone, after all.

After the meal, and when Zosia's friends had gone, Eugenia suggested that they sit round the fire and sang carols. She longed for her piano, but there was no point in pining for it, she must enjoy what she had. She looked at the sparse collection of gifts the girls were opening under the tree. The presents were so few in number compared to other years. Would they be disappointed?

To her relief they seemed content with what they had. Ola was in a high state of excitement and rushed about wearing her fur hat and Halina's crocheted scarf, and Halina was enchanted with the beautiful medallion of the Virgin Mary she and Zosia had given her. Ola's present to her consisted of a picture of everyone, including Kazimierz. The sight of her husband gave her a shock, then she realised Ola was standing by looking at her anxiously. 'Thank you so much Ola,' she said, conjuring up a smile. 'I did not realise you were so talented. The likenesses are very good.'

Ola looked relieved, 'I thought a picture of Papa would cheer you up.'

Eugenia smiled. 'What a nice thought Ola.' However, the picture served to remind her of what she had lost, perhaps for ever.

On one of her rare excursions to the market, Halina had managed to find some small bottles of cologne, which she wrapped in the embroidered handkerchiefs. 'It is not much I know,' Halina handed the tiny parcels to her mother and aunt, 'but Ola and I wanted you to have these.' She was gratified to see her mother's face light up, and watched as she applied the cologne as if it were an expensive perfume from Warsaw.

That night, Halina lay in bed listening to Ola's gentle snores. It had been a strange Christmas - fewer presents, very little food, everything quiet and restrained, but somehow one of her most enjoyable. Everything had been much more intense, and the little ceremonies taken for granted in the past, seemed more significant. She touched the medallion round her neck. Mama and Zosia had little spare money for such luxuries, so she would treasure their gift. She resolved to concentrate on taking as much pleasure as possible from what she had. She did not know how long it would be in her possession.

38

Nine

Eugenia, Halina, Ola, February 1940, Luck

As the days progressed, Eugenia noticed that Soviet soldiers and the NKVD were in evidence wherever she went. There was a large barracks in Luck near the railway station, together with a small airfield, so there was a great deal of activity in the area. At the beginning of February, she was startled by a loud knock at the door. She jumped up nervously, feeling suddenly breathless and faint. Halina and Ola had gone to the market with Zosia to scout for flour and sugar, and she was alone. She opened the door and saw two men in NKVD uniforms. They pushed past her and stood in the hall. Eugenia stood, unable to speak, her heart beating wildly. What did they want? Had they come to arrest her?

'How many live here?' the taller of the two asked.

'Four. My sister and I and my two children.'

'What does your husband do?'

'He went to fight on the German front.' Would the soldiers realise how worried she was?

'What does your sister's husband do?

'He died some years ago.'

While Eugenia was trapped in the hall, the other soldier went into every room and looked round. She knew that Zosia had little of value on show as she either had sold it in the market to buy food, or had hidden it, but she noticed that the second soldier emerged from the living room putting something in his pocket. What had he been doing? He nodded to the first soldier and the pair turned and left as suddenly as they had come.

Eugenia felt very weak, and sat next to the fire, her hands shaking. She had been so sure they were going to arrest her. Thank goodness they had only asked questions. She sat sipping a cup of tea to calm her nerves and looked around her. The clock on the mantel was missing. That must have been what the soldier had put in his pocket. She put down her cup. What would she say to Zosia? The clock was given to her husband on his retirement and it was of great sentimental value to her.

On her return, Zosia was philosophical, 'Better an old clock disappears than my sister and her daughters,' she laughed, but she could not hide from Eugenia just how upset she was.

Men in uniform came to the house regularly over the next few weeks, and asked the same questions about who they were, what the men of the house did and so on. Eugenia repeated the story that her husband had left some time ago and that she had come to live with her sister, as she could not afford to live on her own. She tried to give the soldiers the impression that she had lived in the town for some time, and so far, they seemed satisfied with the explanations. She was very careful to imply that her husband was an enlisted man. Each time however, the experience was more frightening than the last, and by the middle of February, Eugenia was sure that her arrest was inevitable. The local people did not know her. Someone might point her out as a stranger.

Later that week, a letter came for Eugenia, delivered by the cousin of Old Ryszard. Although referred to as Young Ryszard, he was a sprightly but wrinkled man who could have been any age between fifty and eighty. Years of the outside life had given his skin the appearance of animal hide, but small dark buttons of eyes twinkled underneath his bushy grey eyebrows.

'Old Ryszard was given this by that Miron woman you know in Kamionka,' he said, as he sat in the parlour drinking tea and eating some cake. 'She asked Ryszard where you were, but he would not tell 'er. Didn't like the look of 'er he didn't, especially as she had thrown you out, my dear Mrs Korbinska.'

At this, he looked pointedly at the remnants of wine in a bottle, a rare treat that had been carefully nursed to last for several weeks. Eugenia took the hint and poured the few remaining drops into a glass, and he drank the wine eagerly.

'Anyway, she was very anxious you should have this letter. Looked a bit worried she did. And guilty. Quite right too, if you ask me.'

Realising there was no more wine, he stood up, pocketed the few coins Eugenia had given to him and left muttering under his breath, 'Wretched cold weather. These Soviets must have brought it with 'em. Damn Soviets.' He carried on along the street muttering as he went, until his words were absorbed by the thick, white snow that was falling.

Eugenia looked at the letter for a few puzzled moments before she opened it. It was from Veronica Miron.

Dear Eugenia,

I was so sorry you had to leave as you did, but things were becoming difficult. I do hope you have forgiven us. I had to write to you because today two NKVD officers came here. They said they knew that a Mrs Korbinska and her children had stayed here for a time after they had given up their house. They said that Mrs Korbinska was an officer's wife and thus was an enemy of the people. They said they had to find you. They said many other things that I will not bother you with. I did not tell them that you had gone to Luck, but said I knew you had family near Brest and that I thought you had gone there.

Staszek is not here. The Soviets came and said they needed a civil engineer and took him. They did not arrest him, but he had no choice but to go. I am on my own with Adela now, so I understand better what you had to go through. Today I saw some NKVD men looking up at the house. I am afraid, Giena. I am so afraid.

With my love,
Veronica

Eugenia folded the letter. So Veronica Miron had a conscience after all. However, it was very alarming that the NKVD looking for her. How could they know about her? The nightmare was starting again.

Only a few days later, Young Ryszard came to their door again, but this time he had no letter. Eugenia took him into the kitchen and offered him a hot drink, but she noticed that his face looked rather grey and the twinkle in his eyes had dulled.

'What is it Ryszard?'

Ryszard took a sip of the steaming liquid and did not seem to notice that it was too hot to drink. 'My cousin, Old Ryszard, they came for him. The NKVD. His sister told me. They came for him. They said they knew that he was helping people, helping enemies of the people. They said he was a courier and a spy.' He put the cup down and Eugenia saw a sparkle in his eyes once more, but this time it was as a result of tears. 'They hit him with their rifle butts and took him off. Oh my dear lady,' he turned to Eugenia, 'he will not want to tell them about you, but they might hurt him. Who knows what a man will say if hurt enough.'

He stood up, his once straight back bent with despair, 'I am going to stay with my brother near... ...no it is better if I do not tell you where. You are not safe here, you might not be safe.' With that, he lifted his bag and left. This time he did not utter a word as he disappeared into the night.

Eugenia became paler and paler as she listened to his words. The NKVD were getting closer. She turned to her sister, 'Zosia, Ryszard might tell them where we are, even if he does not really want to. What shall I do?'

Zosia took Eugenia firmly by the shoulders. 'You must go to our sister Barbara in the north of the town, at least for a while. She only has a little house so it is unlikely any Soviets would claim it, and it is out of the way on the other side of the lake.'

Eugenia did not have to think for more than a minute before she made her decision. She turned to Halina, 'Go and pack your things, Halina, and help Ola with hers.'

Halina dragged out her case. How many times had she moved now? Was there anywhere safe? She sat for a minute on the bed she had been sharing with Ola and tried hard to swallow a lump that was threatening to choke her. She must not cry. That would just upset Mama more and she had started looking worried again. Ola entered the room and she just managed to smile a little. 'We must pack, Ola, we are going to visit Aunt Barbara's house near the lake.'

'We are not moving again are we,' she complained, 'I don't want to go, I like staying with Auntie Zosia.'

'You get your clothes out of the drawer and we can have a race to see who is ready first.' Halina had relied on sisterly competition saving the day and fortunately, it worked. Ola rushed around dragging clothes from here and there and piled them into a case.

It was too far to walk to Barbara's house, which was over a mile away, but transport was going to be difficult. Eugenia knew that hiring a car would make them conspicuous, and might leave a paper trail that could be followed, even if a car could be found. Zosia solved the problem by borrowing a very old sleigh and equally aged horse belonging to the fisherman she knew.

'No one will notice an old sleigh pulled by an old horse,' she explained to her. There is room for you all plus your bags. If the girls get under the rugs and you wear some old clothes, everyone will think you are a peasant woman on her way to market. I hope.'

The sleigh arrived early the next morning and everything was packed on board. Eugenia had driven a sleigh before, 'but with a much sprightlier horse,' she informed everyone, so the old tired nag was no problem. They said their goodbyes to Zosia, who was sad to see them leave, and set off.

Zosia had plotted a route that avoided the main streets and especially the main areas she thought that the soldiers and the NKVD were staying. It was Sunday morning and there were very few people about. Eugenia thought of Old Ryszard and his comment about the Soviets sleeping off the vodka of the night before and hoped it was true this time as well.

Barbara's house was in a quiet part on the very edge of the town and Eugenia dropped the girls off with the bags so that she could return the sleigh to the part of the river where the fisherman lived. She had a good mile's walk from his hut, but it was important that as few people as possible knew where they had gone. The NKVD were looking for them.

Ten

Eugenia and Kazimierz newly married.
'I am surprised such a beautiful woman as you did not attract the attention of an officer.'

Eugenia, Halina, Ola, March 1940, Luck

Barbara was the youngest of the three sisters. She was very pretty with dark curly hair and the same dark eyes as Eugenia. Halina knew her quite well, as Barbara had stayed with them in Lwow while she was at university there. She had not been married for long and had not yet any children of her own, so she was always pleased to see Halina and Ola when they visited. Her husband had recently obtained a law degree, and had been about to start work at a law firm in Luck when the invasion took place. He now worked 'on a farm somewhere' and was away for most of the day and sometimes at night. Barbara seemed rather vague about where he was working, but he brought home supplies sometimes, for which she was thankful.

The house was very small, and two small bedrooms were a squash for three adults and two children. There was a garden at the back, which Barbara's husband, Titov, used for growing vegetables. There was a large stock of potatoes, onions and carrots in her cellar, although it would soon be demolished with three extra mouths to feed. The vegetables had to share their home with the cases they had brought, as there was no space in the cottage for them.

'They should be all right as long as they are closed tight to keep damp out,' said Eugenia firmly, but by now, they were used to cycling fewer clothes and washing those used each night.

That evening she sat with Barbara in front of the fire. 'It must be difficult for you with Titov away so much,' Eugenia smiled at her sister. The move had gone without a hitch and she was starting to relax again.

'I am glad you came, Giena. I have plenty of friends around, but everyone is so frightened by the talk of arrests, no one goes out much. The NKVD come here now and then to question us, but I think we are too insignificant for them to pay attention to.'

Eugenia felt her mouth go dry. The NKVD were relentless. They might wonder at the sudden arrival of a woman and her daughters. If she thought they were becoming suspicious she would have to leave eastern Poland altogether. Perhaps she would be safer in Warsaw. There were no Soviets there, it seemed. The sick feeling in the pit of her stomach returned. She just had to try not to think about it, but it was so stressful. Halina and Ola seemed to have adapted to their new life and she must try to do the same. She must make the most of the good days and not worry about what might happen. She noticed that Barbara was looking at her and only just managed to force a smile. It was becoming so difficult to keep up the pretence.

April 1940

Halina sat by the window reading a book, wriggling with boredom every now and then as she waited for Easter breakfast to be ready. As she looked out of the window, she saw an NKVD soldier walk up to the house. On frequent occasions, NKVD soldiers came to the house to question them, as they did with most people in the town. Aunt Barbara always made them welcome with offers of tea and cake as if she had nothing to hide. She and Ola usually joined them to make the picture of innocence complete. The men came, took tea and cake, asked some questions and left again. This one looked different from the others and, judging by his uniform, appeared to be an officer. She stood up. She must open the door and invite him in with the politeness Mama had told her was necessary.

Barbara came out of the kitchen and gave a start when she saw the visitor. 'We are about to have Easter breakfast,' she said, recovering quickly and forcing a smile, 'I hope you will join us.'

The man bowed low and replied that he would be delighted.

Halina was taken aback by his courtesy. Their NKVD visitors were usually rough looking and rough spoken. They certainly did not show any respect to them. Not that it stopped them taking the food Barbara offered.

'It is a very modest feast compared to our usual,' started Barbara, and then faltered, wondering if her comment would be seen as a criticism.

'I am looking forward to it,' was the reply, voiced in heavily accented Polish.

The guest was guided towards the seat at the end of the table, while Barbara and Eugenia sat at one side, and Halina and Ola at the other. The meal started with the sharing of hard-boiled eggs, which Ola had painted the night before. She was very proud of her artistry and was especially pleased when the stranger complimented her.

'You are very talented,' he said to Ola, 'did you learn to paint in school?'

'Not really,' replied Ola excitedly, 'I taught myself, but Papa thinks I should concentrate on more serious subjects. I ..,' she stopped suddenly as Halina kicked her under the table.

'Aah. And your husband is away?' he turned to look at Eugenia.

Gripping her napkin tightly under the table to stop her hand shaking, Eugenia replied with the prepared speech she had given many times, 'Yes, he is a soldier and went to fight on the German front some time ago.' She stood up, and then placed a plate of ham and beetroot relish on the table to hide her nervousness.

'I am surprised that a beautiful woman such as you did not attract the attention of an officer.'

'Alas, no, just a soldier – but in the cavalry,' she added.

'And you madam,' he turned to Barbara, 'is your husband also in the army?'

'No, he is working on a farm north of here.' Barbara was more secure in her story as Titov did spend some time working on what was now a collective farm, twenty miles away. He used a chest complaint as an excuse for his frequent absences for Resistance work. He had not told Barbara that he was a Resistance member, but she was too intelligent not to have worked it out for herself.

'Have you always lived with your sister,' the officer turned to Eugenia.

'Just since the war with Germany started,' she explained, 'I did not feel safe on my own with the girls.'

'I understand, of course. This ham is delicious.'

As the Russian spoke to Barbara, Eugenia suddenly remembered that she had not said that she and Barbara were sisters.

They ate the rest of the meal of mazurek cake and a small babka in comparative silence, as the officer told them about his wife who had just arrived, and who was looking forward to seeing round the town.

The Russian was very polite and Halina thought him quite friendly and pleasant. In between mouthfuls, he continued to ask questions in a very casual manner, but somehow managed to discover that she was not at school any more, and that they had spent several years in Lwow.

After the meal, he thanked Barbara and Eugenia politely and started to leave. He turned just as he was about to step outside.

'Madam Korbinska, do you know of a Madam Korbinska, an officer's wife from Kamionka Strumilowa? She has disappeared with her two daughters and we cannot find her. We are concerned for her welfare.'

With that, he left, without waiting for an answer.

When he had gone, they looked at each other for a few moments.

'How did he know we were sisters,' exclaimed Eugenia, 'did you say anything Barbara?'

'Perhaps someone told him,' replied Barbara hesitantly.

'But Mama, that comment about the Korbinskis in Kamionka, that was very strange, especially as he did not wait for a reply,' Halina remarked.

'Yes,' said Eugenia, 'things did not seem right. He almost seemed to know who I was.' In her mind, she imagined the NKVD sitting in front of a large map putting pins in where the Korbinski family had been. First Kamionka, then the Miron's, later Zosia's house and now Barbara's. It did not take her long to make the decision. 'I think it is not safe now, Barbara. We must leave and try to get to Warsaw. Kazimierz will go there looking for us after the war. We agreed that when he left. His mother is alone there in that big house. We should try and go there.'

Barbara came towards her sister and hugged her. The physical contact was brief and light, but helped to fill a small part of the dark void of loneliness and fear that Eugenia felt was now her life.

'Try not to worry Eugenia. I know it is easy for me to say. But look, I am sure my friend Sofia, who lives on her own, will gladly put you up for a few days until you are ready to go to Warsaw. Titov has gone off for a few days and he will not mind if I come with you and introduce you, and perhaps stay a night or two until you are settled. Sofia has a very small house, but it has large cellars. So you can hide if people come asking questions. I have heard that there are guides who will take people over the border. They ask a great deal of money, so you may have to sell everything you have. '

Later, Eugenia sat down in the bedroom with the magnitude of the decision weighing on her. She ran her fingers through her hair and noticed several hairs flutter out and land on the dressing table. She picked one up and looked at it. Was it really her grey hair? Her face looked gaunt and drawn in the mirror and there were lines of strain round her eyes. She gave a wry smile. Would Kazimierz still think her beautiful now?

She looked at the reflection of her hand in the mirror and noticed that she had started to bite her fingernails, something she had not done since she was a child. A flurry of questions floated round and round her head, like so many autumn leaves. Should she go now or wait until she had found a guide to take them over the border? She would have to sell everything to pay for the guide. Would it be safe to go to the market now? She put her hands over her face trying to press back the tears. She had cried so much in the past few months, but it did not help. She must keep strong for the girls. They depended on her and her alone.

They must pack immediately and leave Barbara's house that afternoon. It was Easter Sunday and the roads were quiet.

Eleven

Eugenia, Halina, Ola, April 1940, Luck

Eugenia woke from a troubled dream to find a man standing over her. She started to scream, but he pressed a gloved hand over her mouth. 'Ssh, Giena,' whispered a voice, which she realised belonged to Titov, 'I want you to see this, but I do not want you to wake Sofia or the girls.'

She dressed quickly in several layers of winter clothing at his request and went into the kitchen where she found Barbara putting on her boots.

'I hope Titov did not frighten you, Giena,' she whispered, 'but the children must not see this.'

Eugenia followed Titov out of Sofia's house, down the garden path and along the road, with Barbara close behind. The moon was up and its light was reflected from the snow, so they had no trouble finding their way, although there were no streetlights. They walked for some time until Titov stopped suddenly next to a wall and motioned Eugenia to look carefully over the top, but he did not prepare her for what she saw.

In front of her was a train station. She realised it was the station near the airport and not the one in the centre of town. As far as she could see along the railway line, stood high-sided wooden trucks.

'Cattle trucks,' said Titov, as if he knew what she was about to ask him.

Sleighs, carts and wagons lined the road beside the station, some empty, some piled high with luggage, some piled high with people. There were hundreds of people. Men, women, children, young women with babies, old people, young people. People were sitting in the snow; others were standing next to the tracks. All around were NKVD soldiers carrying rifles with fixed bayonets, herding groups here and there and eventually up into the trucks. She could hear children crying as the moving throng accidentally separated their mothers from them.

Eugenia watched in horror as an old woman, wrapped in what appeared to be bed linen, stumbled and fell. A soldier prodded her with his rifle, but she did not move. Perhaps she did not realise that the bitter cold would freeze her where she lay, perhaps she did not care, but still she lay in the snow. People tripped over her and stood on her, as if she was just an annoying obstacle on the pavement, until two soldiers took hold of her and dragged her to one side where she lay stripped of dignity, humanity and soon her life.

A woman sat cradling her young baby, but the body was stiff and cold. A long sleigh journey on a bitterly cold night had taken his life, and she could not bring it back no matter how she cried and wept and caressed his lifeless body.

The soldiers pushed groups of forty or fifty people, sometimes more, into each truck. From the cries that carried through the night, it was obvious that some wives and husbands, mothers and children had become separated. A woman started screaming the names of her children, and she ran along the tracks, stopping at each truck and looking up at the tiny grilles in the wagon sides. A soldier hit her with his rifle butt, but still she screamed out her children's names, until eventually he forced her up into another wagon, blood streaming down the side of her face.

More sleighs arrived, and people climbed out, tripping over the weight of the bags and cases they were carrying, their faces showing shock, confusion and sheer terror.

Eugenia could not bear to watch the spectacle in front of her, but neither could she tear herself away. Her instinct was to run over and help, but she could do nothing, only watch impotently.

'Titov, what is happening,' she finally managed to say, the words hardly audible with the sobs that came unbidden from deep inside.

'Deportation,' he said, 'probably to Siberia. All those people were dragged from their homes at dead of night to travel in freezing cold trucks for miles and miles and miles. We are so afraid they will end up in labour camps like those the Tsar used when he invaded Poland all those years ago. They will be worked slowly and painfully to death.'

Ola heard her mother get up and leave the room. Where on earth was she going? Eugenia disappeared through the back door, leaving it unlocked. Ola quickly pulled on several of her thickest sweaters, struggling to fit her winter coat over them. She found her boots and put them on together with scarf, hat and gloves. It looked very cold outside, but she had to find out what Mama was doing out in the middle of the night. There was no other excitement these days. She opened the back door and followed the moonlit footsteps clearly visible in the snow.

Soon she saw her mother standing behind a wall with Auntie Barbara and Uncle Titov, and she moved behind a bush so she could see what they were looking at. What a disappointment! It was just lots of trains and people. But everyone looked very pale in the station lights, and they all had a strange look on their face. Rather like that on Eva Paschwa's face just before she had thrown up all over her desk in class. But there did not seem to be much excitement, just a lot of people getting on a train. She turned to go back the way she had come. She must tread carefully, stepping in the snowy footsteps. She did not want her outing to be discovered.

Twenty minutes later, she lay shivering in bed, her snowy boots hidden in a corner in the kitchen. Why could she not forget what she had seen? It was only people and trains. But they did look very frightened. And it looked as if a soldier hit someone with his gun. No. It was just people and trains. Nothing to be afraid of. But why was Mama there?

Eugenia could take no more. She turned to go back to Sofia's house and Titov followed her. He stopped her just inside the door of the house as Barbara pushed past, her eyes streaming with tears.

'Eugenia, I had to show you that, so you would know the danger you are in. If you had not left yesterday, you might have been with them. You are an officer's wife – some of those on that train are officer's wives. I heard that the NKVD came to our house last night and I am sure they were looking for you. We must thank God that you were at Sofia's, and that there was no one at home. We think they are trying to remove everyone who has any status, education or position in Poland. They are trying to destroy the heart of our country.'

With that, he was gone.

'What do you mean "we" think,' Eugenia began to ask, but the answer came to her just as the door closed. Titov might work on a farm somewhere in the countryside, but he was in the Polish Resistance.

48

Two days later, Eugenia was still shocked by what she had seen, and as she sat at the breakfast table, she could not forget the sight. She knew that the Tsar had deported Poles before he was deposed, and had even heard rumours of recent deportations in other parts of Poland, but the reality was more terrible than her imagination had allowed. All those people had been treated worse than cattle. Nothing but indifference at best, and cruelty at worst from the soldiers and the NKVD. She toyed with her toast. Just when she thought things could not get worse, this happened. The thought of arrest was bad enough, but deportation! It was a terrifying thought.

She looked at Ola, but she was avoiding her eyes, which was strange. What if her children were put on those awful trucks and taken off to the frozen wastes of Siberia? She could not let that happen. Halina kept glancing in her direction. Should she tell Halina? She was becoming much more mature these days, and had coped so well with the changes, but should she burden her with this knowledge? But if she did not tell her, she might find out from someone else; everyone in the town would know soon, and Sofia would talk about nothing else. Thankfully, Sofia was having her breakfast in bed, happy to have people to wait on her. She could not protect Halina any longer from the truth. She had to tell her. It was such a strain having to keep it quiet.

She finished her breakfast, left Ola playing a game with Barbara, and told Halina to put on her warmest clothes and to follow her. As they walked towards the station, she gave Halina an abridged version of what she had seen that night.

The train with its terrible cargo had pulled out only a few hours before. The soldiers had removed the bodies by the roadside, for which Eugenia was grateful, but a torn, bloodied scrap of linen fluttered on the edge of the station fence, defying the icy wind's attempt to freeze it rigid.

Most of the sleighs and wagons had gone, but there were still one or two soldiers around, although they made no move to stop anyone coming closer. Several people wandered up and down the track, picking up scraps of paper that had been thrown out of the grilles of the departing wagons. Halina picked up a piece and read it. It was an impassioned plea from a woman asking the reader to tell her daughter that she had been taken. The woman's name and address, and that of her daughter were written below. The tone of the writing was so intense she could almost feel the desperation of the writer, who had been dragged off without having the chance to tell her daughter what had happened. She put the paper in her pocket. There was always a faint possibility she could deliver it.

The weight of human traffic had melted the snow beside the tracks, but it was now frozen, here and there encasing patches that were stained red. At intervals between the tracks, were frozen piles surrounded by frozen yellow snow. Halina realised in disgust that the yellow was urine and the piles were of human excrement, obviously originating from the cattle trucks that must have been standing for many hours, full of people and with the doors locked shut. How dreadful to be shut in and degraded in such a way. No wonder Mama looked so upset; it must have been awful to see people treated so badly. It was even frightening now, and the trains had gone.

'Mama, what happened here?' Halina asked, her voice trembling, 'could this happen to us?'

'I will do whatever I can to make sure it does not, Halina,' replied Eugenia as tears gathered once more, 'We must be so careful. You have your father's proud air, Halina. You must always try to look humble, try to be overlooked, and try to be ignored.'

'Now I know what to do, Barbara,' Eugenia said when she had returned home, 'I will go to the market to find a guide. We cannot stay here any longer and put you in danger. If we had not left on Sunday......'

Halina jumped as her mother shut the door with a bang and rushed out of the house. The trip to the station had upset her, but she found it hard to imagine how it would have looked with hundreds and hundreds of people massing together. She picked up a poetry book and tried to escape to a world of love and beauty.

Ola was sitting on the other side of the window with her drawing book. As Ola stood up to retrieve an errant pencil, Halina noticed a picture she had not seen before. 'What is that, Ola,' she said, looking at a picture of high-sided trucks with people standing round.

''Portations,' Ola replied, looking guilty.

'Deportations!' exclaimed Halina, 'How could you have seen the deportations? Mama has not let you anywhere near the station, and even I did not see the cattle trucks.'

'I followed Mama and Uncle Titov and Auntie Barbara when they went out that night.'

'I don't believe it! Ola, what on earth were you thinking!'

'I was thinking I wanted to know what was going on.' Ola replied firmly, but Halina noticed her hand was shaking.

'Well I won't tell Mama, but Ola you must not go out like that again. It was very cold that night. You might have frozen to death.'

'Well I didn't. Anyway, I know how cold Poland is. Really Halina, you are beginning to sound just like Papa.' With that, Ola took her book and marched out of the room.

Halina looked in astonishment as Ola closed the door. Little Ola. Going out in the middle of the night. She was not such a baby after all.

Eugenia met the guide in a small alleyway and listened as he told her how many families he had managed to get over the border. 'It is so good to see the faces of the children when they realise they are free,' he said, pulling his hat further down over his ears. He told her the route they would be taking that night. 'We will take a train to a place near the River Bug and then stay in a hut until midnight. Once I have checked it is safe, we will walk the last mile to the river. There will be a boat to take us across the border and then we will be able to travel to Warsaw. We will rest in huts and safe houses along the way and travel at night. The Polish resistance will help us once we are over the border.'

Eugenia looked at the man who could be her salvation. Could she trust him? He was asking so much money, but some of the other guides asked even more. However, if she knew about him, did the NKVD also know what he did? The guide pulled her into the shadows as some soldiers walked by. On the other hand, he knew about the Polish Resistance, which was a good sign. She had no choice. She had to trust him. She promised she would pay the 50,000 roubles he asked for and arranged to leave Luck that night.

'He is asking a great deal of money – tens of thousands of roubles,' Eugenia said to Halina, as she told him of her meeting with the guide. 'Thank goodness I still have things to sell. Come with me to the market this morning, Halina. We want to sell what is left as quickly as possible.'

Having separated out the items to be sold, which was most of what they had, they loaded them onto a cart and set out for the market in Luck. Eugenia had saved her best jewellery until that point and had taken it to someone Barbara said would give her a good price. Halina laid out evening gowns, bed linen and the assortment of clothes she had to sell. It was humiliating standing in the market selling clothes. How had Mama managed to look so cheerful about it?

The Soviet girls were already picking through everything. Like vultures. She would just have to grit her teeth and hope they would not be able to tell what she was thinking about them. She held up the blue silk backless dress that had been her mother's favourite, shook it out and showed it to a Soviet girl who looked puzzled by the lack of a back panel.

'Was there not enough material to finish the dress?' she asked.

Halina said grandly, 'That is the latest fashion. If you wear this you will be the most elegant woman around.' She handed the girl a fine woollen shawl. 'This will cover the bare back if it is cold. That way you will be warm as well as elegant.'

The girl, unused to such quality of style and material, eagerly snatched them up, paid what Halina asked and ran off carrying the gown as if it were a child. Halina watched her go in disgust. That coarse, clumsy girl would look stupid in that dress. Mama had looked so beautiful in it. How could she bear to let it go? She looked at the pile of roubles the girl had given her. She felt rather like Judas with thirty pieces of silver.

A fat little Soviet girl picked up Ola's prized doll Anna, and stood open-mouthed with wonder at the beautiful object. That was the doll she had before Ola. Her first doll. One of her treasured childhood memories and that girl was about to take it off. She found it hard to resist the temptation to snatch it back.

Everything was selling so quickly, she did not have much time to think, and before she knew it, the table was almost bare. Her mother's silken shawl lay forlornly on the table. She could not part with that. She had to keep something of Mama's. She pushed it into her pocket aware of the faint scent of perfume still clinging to it. Soon she was left with an empty table and an even emptier heart. Eugenia returned a few minutes later to the sight of Halina looking unusually miserable.

'It was just things, Halina,' she said, putting her arms round her daughter, 'things that can be replaced. We can make do with what we have until the war is over, and then we can start again.'

Halina touched the shawl in her pocket and tried to smile at her mother. Would the war ever be over?

That afternoon Halina took a small bag upstairs to pack the few items she had left. Mama had said she could only take a small bag, as she would not be able to carry anything bigger. Her spare underwear, a change of clothing and some bread were essential, but once they were packed, there was very little room. It would be so difficult to decide what else to take with her, as each item had memories attached firmly to it. She opened the little tinder box in which she had placed Edmond's flint and the family photographs. She picked up the flint, unwrapped the cloth covering it, and traced the sharp contours with her fingers. She could not leave Papa's box behind. It was all she had to remind her of him. That and the photographs. Besides, she might have to light a fire someday. The silken shawl she had kept from the market sale was unceremoniously squashed into a tiny corner and she took it out again just to reassure herself it would spring back into shape. She would have to take that. It did not take up much room and it was still scented with Mama's perfume. She would wear her school uniform and thick school coat. They were dark and would blend into the darkness, and the thick woollen coat would keep her warm. It had become much warmer in the last day or two, but was still cold. And that was it. She shut the bag. She would have to shut her emotions inside too. Mama and Ola needed her support.

Just two hours later, she was walking towards the station with Ola and Eugenia. She looked back at the faces of Sofia and Barbara pressed close to the window. She hated having to leave yet again, but perhaps this time they would find somewhere safe.

The guide had told Eugenia that the most dangerous part of the journey was at the beginning. He told her he would pretend to be her husband, and say they had been visiting relatives over Easter, should anyone ask. He had bought the tickets for them, which was fortunate, as Eugenia had worried that if she bought tickets it might attract unwelcome attention. The train was in the station when they arrived and the guide hustled them into the third class carriage at the end of the train.

They sat and waited nervously for the train to leave. Someone in a railway uniform checked their tickets and looked them over, but there was no obvious sign of the NKVD. They sat on wooden benches crammed in the carriage with a large group. There were very few Polish speakers in the carriage and most seemed Ukrainian. That heightened Eugenia's anxiety, as she felt rather conspicuous. After an agonisingly long time, the train finally moved out of the station, and she breathed again. Now there was some hope.

Twelve

Eugenia, Halina, Ola, April 1940, Luck

The train journey was without incident, although Eugenia told Halina that her heart was beating so loudly she could hardly hear the noise of the train on the tracks. They changed trains at Kiwerce to the main north south railway, where they travelled north, and then again onto a local line which brought them closer to the new Soviet/Polish border.

The guide was obviously very experienced in taking refugees on the route as he showed a total lack of nerves, which had a calming effect on the little group. Now and then, he talked to Ola and Halina, whispering that they would soon see their grandmother in Warsaw. Ola was the most comforted by this, Eugenia was too nervous to hope too much, but Halina rather disliked the little man – all she could think of was that her mother had sold all of her jewels in order to pay him.

'Why do you want to go to Warsaw,' he asked, his eyes not meeting hers as he spoke, 'Germans are all over the place.'

'My father is an officer and we are afraid of being arrested if we stay here.'

The guide nodded understandingly at this and said that he had taken several such families over the border and away from the Soviets. Halina thought his speech was just a little too well prepared.

It was late evening when they left the train and walked into the darkness. They walked for a mile along a narrow track and eventually came upon a hut surrounded by pine trees and situated on the edge of a wood.

'Wait in here until around midnight, when I will return,' the guide instructed, 'There is water and food in the hut. You will be quite safe here.' With that, he disappeared into the darkness.

They entered the hut and found a wooden table on which, sure enough, was some water, bread and cheese. Halina and Ola ate with relish, but Eugenia only drank a little water. They settled themselves on the wooden benches ranged against the wall and began their wait until midnight.

Halina woke with a start as her head slipped down the wall on which she was leaning. Ola was fast asleep, held tightly in her mother's arms. Her mother looked pale, but her eyes were very bright. Was it tears? She thought back to the day of her father's departure. It had been much more difficult than she had expected when he left. He had looked so pleased to see her when he saw that she had come to say goodbye. She smiled. All that time she had thought he had not loved her. But that was just his strict manner. Underneath he really did love her; he just found it difficult to show it. Why had it taken her so long to work it out?

She sat up suddenly. He had not just said goodbye, he was saying it might be his last goodbye. Had it needed the possibility of death before he could display emotion to her? When she saw him again, she would ask him. When he came to Warsaw. Would she really be safer there? Mama had said that they had nothing to lose, as they faced certain arrest or deportation if they stayed. What if things were as bad or worse? She sat back against the wall. There was no point in thinking like that; of course Papa would go to Warsaw when the war was over. She would see him again.

Suddenly, she heard a noise outside and held her breath for a moment

'Mama,' she whispered. 'I think he is back.'

Eugenia's eyes opened wider as she gradually rose to her feet, gently disentangling herself from Ola. They stood facing the door. Halina's heart raced and then was clutched with relief as the guide pushed the door open and entered the cabin.

'Get ready to go now,' he said 'It is midnight. There is a moon out there so we should be able to move closer to the river without needing lights.'

Halina picked up her coat and her bag with its few possessions. Eugenia woke Ola who rose sleepily, frowning slightly as she tried to remember what was happening. She saw Halina with her bag in her hand and picked up her own. 'Are we…'

'Ssh,' said Eugenia, 'we must be quiet now Ola dear, there might be some Soviet soldiers around here.'

Ola looked as if she was about to start crying and Halina felt a slight nag of impatience, before feeling guilty almost immediately. Ola was still very young after all. The guide held the door open as they filed out. The moonlit night seemed very bright after the darkness of the cabin, and the recent thaw meant that it was not too cold.

'It is not far to the river,' the guide said. 'I will check that the boat has arrived when we get closer, and then we can go down to the water.'

As they walked out into the night, Halina noticed how darkness had softened shapes and sounds. The hard rustling edges of the bushes had transformed into rounded, whispering masses, and the solid, dark mass of the pine trees had taken on the quality of velvet. She looked up at the moon, which was almost full. Was Papa looking up at the same moon?

They walked past some railings and inside she saw some gravestones. They cast long dark shadows in the moonlight pointing towards the hut they had just left. Halina shivered. The shadows of the gravestones looked so sinister. On the other hand, perhaps it was the thought of the uncertainties ahead that made her hands feel so cold. As she walked past the railing, she noticed that the path was thick with pine needles and her feet made very little noise.

Ola was holding her mother's hand tightly, stumbling every now and then as she encountered an unexpected bump in the path. She seemed very small and innocent as her bag bumped her legs with each step, and looked so vulnerable. Eugenia turned round to make sure she was following, and smiled at her. She felt a little happier. Mama was not worried so it must be safe.

The path followed the edge of the forest where pine trees rose forbiddingly on one side, and the moon blinked off and on as it disappeared and reappeared behind the trees. Halina walked for about twenty minutes until in the distance she could see a silver ribbon in the moonlight, where the line of trees ended. They were nearly there. Her heart beat a little faster and the earlier tiredness vanished.

'It's the river, Mama,' she whispered.

The guide stopped. 'Wait here,' he said, 'I will go on ahead and make sure the boat has arrived. Don't worry children, you will soon be on the other side and on your way.'

Although annoyed at being called a child, Halina felt a frisson of excitement and shivered again a little, despite the relative warmth of the night air.

Suddenly a rustling behind her, made her heart thud. She turned round and saw a metal rod shining in the moonlight. She followed the rod along its length and looked up straight into the face of a Soviet soldier. 'Mama,' she started to say and turned round quickly, only to see three more soldiers standing round pointing their guns at them. Suddenly through her mind passed all the stories she had heard of people being shot by Soviet soldiers. She closed her eyes, expecting any minute to hear a shot, and was relieved when their captors spoke.

'Where are you going now on a fine night like this,' the tallest of the soldiers said, 'I think we need to talk about this.'

'Trying to cross the border are you – well now you are under arrest,' said another.

Halina looked at her mother who stood unable to speak. 'Oh no,' was all she managed to say.

The guide suddenly appeared in the distance coming from the direction of the river. 'Shoot him,' said the officer with the group. The nearest soldier raised his gun and fired, the report causing Halina to jump and Ola to cry loudly. The guide fell to the ground.

The soldiers then proceeded to prod the trio with their rifles, forcing them to walk back the way they had come. As Halina had travelled towards the river, hope had lightened her step and the half hour walk had seemed easy. Now tiredness and despair engulfed her, and she stumbled as she retraced her steps. What would happen to them now?

Eventually they came to a tall building of stone and wood that looked like a town hall. They were shepherded roughly up the steps and inside, where a narrow corridor led to a square room holding a wooden table at which sat two soldiers. They were taken to a hard wooden bench in the corner, and Eugenia was called over to the table to stand in front of the soldiers. A long interrogation started which lasted the rest of the night.

Thirteen

Eugenia, Halina, Ola, April 1940, Brest

'What is your name?'

Eugenia heard the question for the fifth time that night and for the fifth time she gave her maiden name.

'Frank.'

She had decided to give only her maiden name of Frank as she remembered that the NKVD officer in Luck had known her as Korbinska, but as the night wore on, one of the soldiers caught her out.

'You are Mrs Korbinska, no?'

She started to say no, but she was so shocked at hearing her name that her face gave her away. Perhaps I should admit to it, she thought in despair, perhaps, that way if Kazimierz comes looking for me he will recognise the name and not think it someone else.

'You are Mrs Korbinska?'

'Yes,' she said. She was too exhausted to argue.

'Is your husband in the army?'

'Yes.'

'Is he an officer?'

'No, he is an enlisted man.'

'Where are you going tonight?'

'To visit my mother in law in Warsaw.'

'Do you know it is an offence to cross the Soviet border?'

'No.'

And so it continued for hours and hours. The same questions over and over again until Eugenia started to sway on her feet with exhaustion. She was feeling faint from lack of food, but it was only when she staggered and nearly fell that the soldiers told her to sit down.

They called Halina next for questioning, and Eugenia was distraught. Surely they were not going to give the same treatment to Halina; she was only a girl. But there was nothing she could do to stop it.

Halina stood up and walked towards the soldiers. Mama had been tearful, her voice breaking with strain as she had attempted to answer the soldiers' questions. She was not going to give them the satisfaction of seeing her cry like her mother. In fact, she was angry. Those ignorant soldiers had upset Mama. She would show them what a Polish heroine could be like.

As a soldier came towards Halina and indicated that she was to be interrogated next, he pointed to the medallion of the Virgin Mary that she wore round her neck. 'What is that?' he asked.

'It is the Virgin Mary,' Halina replied.

He made a sound of disgust, snatched it from her neck and threw it on the ground where it lay forlornly. Halina glared at the soldier. How dare he throw away her medallion! What was more annoying, she could do nothing about it. As the soldier pushed her towards the table where her interrogators sat, she put her shoulders back, raised her chin a little higher and glared defiantly at them.

'What is your name?' the tall fair one asked.

'Halina Korbinska,' she said loudly and clearly.

'Where are you going?'

'To visit my grandmother in Warsaw.'

'Do you normally travel on foot in the middle of the night?' he asked

She did not answer.

The next question came from the shorter, darker of the two who spoke more gently than his colleague did.

'We know your father is a Polish officer,' he said and then added with a conspiratorial wink, 'I expect he is a colonel.'

Halina mustered all the contempt she could, 'No, he is a general,' she replied.

Eugenia gasped at the audacity of her daughter's response and feared for reprisals. To her surprise, the soldiers seemed amused by the response, or perhaps they even respected it. She realised that they had deliberately been trying to trick Halina into admitting that her father was an officer, but suspected that they already knew.

'What a girl, what a girl,' the soldiers said to each other, a smile threatening to lift the corners of their mouths. Eugenia was overcome with relief.

They continued for another two hours to ask Halina the same questions repeatedly, but her courage did not fail and she gave the same answers each time, although with a little less contempt as she realised all too quickly that she had fallen into their trap.

By the time the interrogation had finished, it was morning. Eugenia was chalk white, with dark smudges under her eyes, and she felt tired and dirty. She put her arms round Ola who had cried intermittently throughout the night. Now she was very quiet. Through a window she could see that the sun was rising, but not on freedom as she had hoped. She had failed to protect her daughters. She had chosen a guide who had not kept them safe, but what was worse, they had been tricked into admitting her husband was an officer, when it appeared that the guards knew it all along. It was her fault that they had been arrested. Guilt consumed her.

The guards returned and took them outside into a waiting wagon where they spent an uncomfortable half hour bouncing around in the back, before stopping once again. They climbed out of the wagon into the sunshine and found themselves outside a large red brick building.

'I know this place,' Eugenia whispered, 'it is Brest Fort. Polish army garrisons are stationed here.' She faltered as she realised that there would be no Polish soldiers there now, except perhaps as prisoners. It was now used by Soviet troops.

She looked around and saw soldiers and vehicles in front of the building. No one paid them any attention as they were pushed through a door and then to a room upstairs at the front of the building. The guard unlocked a door and pushed them inside before locking it noisily.

Eugenia stood with an arm round each of her daughters. They were in a large room with twenty or thirty other people, all women and children. A woman came up to her and greeted her, took her by the hands and drew her to a vacant seat near the window.

'Sit down, my dear, you look exhausted. I am Irena. Have you just been interrogated? It is very frightening is it not.' Irena carried on talking quietly to Eugenia, asking questions but not really expecting answers.

'We paid someone to take us over the border, but we were caught and the guide was shot,' she said eventually.

Irena grimaced, 'That is the same story for most of us here,' she looked around at the other woman several of whom nodded. 'There is no doubt we have been betrayed.'

Every family there had a similar story to tell. They had paid a large sum of money to a guide who had promised to take them over the border to western Poland.

'They were so nice to the children,' said one woman, 'telling them that soon they would see their Grandma. They told us that there were few Germans around over the border and that we would be safe. They seemed so genuine.'

Halina stood at window squinting at the sun that shone through, highlighting the dirt on the glass. She cleared a small area and looked out. There were Soviet soldiers and vehicles moving around outside - dark shapes with the sun behind them edging them in gold. As she looked, a figure came out of the fort, and rode off on a bicycle. As he approached, the sun lit up his face. It was the guide. The guide they had seen shot in the forest.

'Mama, look,' she said urgently, 'Look who it is - it is our guide.'

Eugenia moved to the window. 'You are right Halina, I think it is him. The shooting was set up to make us think he was really on our side. All the time he had planned to betray us. He betrayed us for money. All that money.' She paused for a moment. 'That explains how those soldiers knew so much about us. I was sure they knew your father was an officer from the way they questioned me. That man must have told them. No doubt he will go back to Luck and tell Barbara that we passed safely over the border, and then more families will be betrayed.'

Ola spoke for the first time that day. 'I'm hungry,' she said sounding so miserable that Eugenia's heart went out to her.

'Do they feed us here?' she asked one of the women.

'Oh yes,' she said bitterly, 'We get soup and bread with some hot water if we are lucky.'

As she spoke, the door rattled again as a key was turned and a guard came in with a tray of bread and water that he handed to the nearest woman, before turning and slamming the door shut. Eugenia had difficulty in eating as she was still very upset, but eventually she took a piece of bread and nibbled it listlessly.

They stayed for a week in the fort, with several more families joining them and telling the same story of betrayal. After a few days, one by one the members of the group left the room. They left and did not return. Those who remained became increasingly nervous, as fear of the unknown gripped them. So far, Halina had remained almost unaffected by the trauma, as she was so full of anger at their arrest. The anger had burned within her and had driven out any other emotions, but eventually she became affected by the atmosphere of fear. Each time the door opened, everyone stopped and turned as one. When the door closed again, those left behind relaxed a little. But it was for a short while only, as the relief once more gave way to fearful imagination of what might be.

Finally, after days of emotional ups and downs, the door opened and the Korbinska name was called out with several others. They collected their small bags, said a brief farewell to those remaining, and left.

Barbara, May 1940, Luck

'It is so good of you to help me, dear,' Sofia took the cup offered her by Barbara, 'and you are welcome to stay as long as you like.'

Since Eugenia and the girls had left Luck, Barbara had continued staying with Sofia. The visit by the NKVD to her house had worried her and she was afraid they might deport her for being related to Eugenia. Titov was absent for longer and longer periods and was happier that she was not on her own. He openly admitted that he was in the Resistance now, but never told her anything about his work. She did not ask, as she knew it was safer for him – what she did not know, she could not divulge if interrogated.

Every week she returned to her house to check that all was well and to put some heat into the house to prevent damp. Titov left her notes from time to time, either delivered by himself or one of his colleagues. He put them behind a brick in the cellar wall 'for safety' as he put it. She checked each time she left after a day at the house, and was pleased to find one that evening. After returning to Sofia's and making her a drink, she sat next to the fire to read at her leisure.

The letter started with the usual declarations of love that two years of marriage had not diminished. She blushed in the firelight and hoped that Sofia would not ask what was in the letter. After the first page, the colour drained from her face as she read:

> Barbara, I have some upsetting news for you. I have discovered that Eugenia and the girls have been arrested and taken to Brest prison. We are not sure where they were taken afterwards but we are trying to find out. Young girls of Ola's age are usually sent to the children's home north of Brest, but Eugenia and possibly Halina, will probably be deported. If you want to write to Kazimierz' mother and cousin in Warsaw to tell them, leave the letter in the usual place and I will try to get one of the couriers to take it across the border. The Resistance in German-occupied Poland has become well organised and, all being well, the letter should arrive safely.

Barbara put down the letter. 'Oh no,' she cried aloud, her eyes starting to fill, 'after all that time evading the NKVD, she is taken so near to escaping.'

'Is everything all right, Barbara dear?' Sofia was alert as ever to news and tried to offer some words of reassurance, once Barbara had told her the content of the letter.

'Titov said he will try and find out what has happened to them, Sofia. I do hope it is not deportation.' She wiped her tears and sat down at the writing desk to write to Kazimierz' cousin Janina in Warsaw. 'I cannot see that they will be able to do anything,' she explained to Sofia, 'but they will want to know.' She took up her pen and started to write,

> My Dear Janina,
> Today I have had some very bad news……..'

Fourteen

Eugenia, Halina, May 1940, Brest Prison

The guards escorted the prisoners out of the fort, and pushed them into the back of a waiting wagon. There were several in the group, all women and children. There were one or two girls about Halina's age and she talked quietly to them about her experiences. The other women said very little, and Eugenia spoke only to Ola, who had remained very quiet during her time in the fort.

After about half an hour's drive, they stopped outside a forbidding stone building with large gates.

'It looks like a prison,' someone said.

'At least it is a Polish prison,' said another.

They were led into a large room where sat several officials - obviously Soviet. Eugenia looked around nervously, wondering what would happen next. She was physically and emotionally exhausted after months of trying to protect her daughters and found it impossible to stop guilt from eating at her. She heard the name Korbinska and grabbing hold of her daughters, followed a guard with another bringing up the rear. They stopped in front of a small cell and were told to go inside. Ola started to follow, but the guard stopped her. Eugenia turned, and suddenly realised that Ola was not going with them.

'No,' she screamed and tried to hold onto Ola, 'Not my little Ola, please she is just a child.'

Ola started screaming, 'Mama.'

The guard was young and unlike some of the more brutal soldiers she had seen. He spoke gently to Eugenia and told her that Ola was too young to go to prison. She would have to go to a children's home where she would be educated. Eugenia continued crying for them to leave Ola with her, but it was useless. The guards left, pulling Ola who was still screaming, 'Mama, Mama don't let them take me.' The door slammed shut, and Eugenia sank to the floor.

Halina stood, uncertain and unsure. One of the women in the cell gently lifted Eugenia to her feet and helped her onto the bunk. 'We keep the bunks for those who need them most,' she said to Halina.

There were about twenty other women and girls in the cell. There was not much room, but there was space to sit down and Halina sat on the concrete floor in a corner. Hanging from the ceiling was a light bulb that highlighted the dust that swirled and eddied each time someone moved. There were two double bunks at each side with nothing in between. In the corner, she could see a bucket from which came a strong smell of urine.

'We have to use that, I'm afraid,' the woman who had helped her mother was speaking. 'I am Maria and you are?'

'Halina and my mother is Eugenia.'

'We are allowed out to wash and to go to the toilet once a day, but the rest of the time we have to use the bucket. We try to use it just for urine – anything else makes it very unpleasant for everyone else, you understand.'

Halina tried not to look at the bucket. Her bladder was telling her she needed to use it, but it would be so embarrassing. Everyone would be able to see her and hear her. Perhaps she could wait.

Somehow, Maria knew what was going through her mind. 'You will soon get used to it,' she said, kindly. 'If you like I will stand in front of you to give you some privacy. I am a nurse, so you need not be ashamed.'

Halina stood up. It was no good. She just had to use the bucket. The alternative would be much worse. Maria was very kind and understood how she felt, but it did not make the experience any less humiliating, and when she had finished, her cheeks were flaming. She looked over at the bunk on which Eugenia lay, with her arms round her knees. She was rocking backwards and forwards moaning and crying 'Ola, Ola, they've taken my little Ola,' but her eyes were dry. What could she do?

She had never seen Mama so upset. She put her arms round her and murmured, 'I am still here Mama, and it is all right. It will be all right,' but she did not seem to hear her and continued rocking and moaning. A little later, soup and bread was pushed into the cell and Halina tried to get Eugenia to drink some soup, but she simply turned her head away. She felt frightened for the first time since the invasion. If her mother lost her mind, she would be alone. It was a terrifying thought. She felt sick.

One of the girls who was about her age, came over to speak to her and Halina was glad of the distraction. 'Hello, Halina, I am Bella. Were you also caught trying to cross the so-called border?'

Halina nodded.

Bella continued, 'I was arrested for that too, but they do not know I am a courier for the Resistance.'

Halina turned towards the girl, her interest piqued despite the circumstances. 'What did you do, were you really a courier?'

'Yes, but of course I would never admit that to the NKVD. That would make me a political prisoner and political prisoners are tortured, we think.'

Halina was astonished at the matter of fact way in which the girl spoke. The question of torture had never crossed her mind and the knowledge increased her anxiety.

'But they do not torture people just for crossing the border,' Bella added hurriedly when she saw the expression on Halina's face. 'Some of the Polish army managed to escape the Germans and the Soviets and live in the forests. We take them food and carry messages for them. They are helped by others who are still free. Maria over there for example, is a nurse for us. She lost her job when her hospital was closed and shipped off to Russia, and was keen to help the Resistance. Some of the sabotage the Resistance carries out is very dangerous and there are many injuries – we need nurses.'

As Bella talked, Halina thought of her father and hoped against hope that he was one of those who had escaped.

That night she lay on the bunk with her arms round her mother. It was impossible to sleep. The cell was very warm and everyone was stripped to underwear. The air was stuffy and laden with body odours. Worst of all, the light stayed on throughout the night. The bulb that seemed dim during the day now seemed as bright as the sun. She closed her eyes, but still the light burned. She would never get to sleep. The light was too bright and she was hungry, so, so hungry, tired, dirty and frightened. Hot tears scalded her cheek. No one would be able to see her crying if she turned towards the wall. Mama, Mama, please get better.

The next day, Halina persuaded her mother to take a little soup and bread and even to walk to the toilet they were allowed to use once a day, but still, on her return, she sat in the corner rocking back and forth saying, 'Ola, they took my little Ola,' over and over. Halina had never felt so helpless. She had lost her father. She had lost her sister. She had lost her home. She could not bear to lose her mother. She had to do something.

Finally, she knelt down beside her and grabbed her shoulders. 'Mama,' she said, 'Mama, look at me. I am still here. I need you. Mama, please, I need you. Do not go away from me.' She repeated it several times, each time grabbing a little tighter. After what seemed like an eternity, Eugenia finally turned and looked at her. For the first time since she arrived, she looked at her daughter and saw her. 'Halina,' she said, 'Halina, I am so sorry.'

Halina folded her mother in her arms and the two of them lay in an embrace that lasted for several long minutes. Eventually, Eugenia got to her feet, unsteady after her days of limited motion. 'I am so stiff,' she said, trying to inject a laugh into her voice, but her eyes were flat, the only traces of their trademark shine were the remnants of tears of despair.

Eugenia functioned automatically for several days. The women in the cell were supportive and encouraged her to join in the communal prayers that took place each evening, but she did not start to recover fully until she found Ola's socks. She reached into her bag one morning for her spare underwear when her hand brushed something soft. She brought out a pair of woollen socks. Ola's socks. She had not had time to give them to her before she had been taken away. Eugenia looked at the socks unable to move. Ola was gone. She might never find her again. She sat down on the bunk and held the socks to her face. Her little Ola was gone.

Out of the corner of her eye, she could see Halina watching her anxiously. She smiled at her to reassure her that she would not break down again. Halina must have been so frightened. She had frightened herself. She reached out and stroked Halina's hair. Halina thought she had broken down because of Ola's departure, but it was just the final straw. It was the accumulation of months of tension, months of worrying about Kazimierz, months of playing cat and mouse with the NKVD, months of not knowing if or when she was going to be arrested. Now that it had finally happened, it was almost a relief. The worst had happened and she was still in one piece.

But had the worst happened? Eugenia put the socks back in her bag. She could not think about that. She would not let herself break down again, whatever happened. She smiled at Halina again. She still had one daughter and must think of her. Her smile faded. But was Ola safe?

'Mama,' Halina said, still anxious about her mother's state of mind, 'we must try and find out where Ola has gone, then we can look for her after the war.'

'Do you think we could?' Eugenia saw a tiny piece of hope and clung tightly to it.

'Yes of course. I will ask everyone I see if they know of any children's homes near Brest, and you can ask the guards.'

An elderly woman sitting next to them laughed, 'You have some hope thinking the guards will care. They have no feelings, that lot.'

'But at least we can try,' Halina rounded on her, 'and Mama can speak Russian which might help'

'Sorry, dear.' The older woman did not expect such a spirited response and concentrated hard on a piece of bread she had in her hand.

Halina spoke to everyone in the cell, but no one came from the area and thus could not help. Contact with the other prisoners was limited and restricted to visits to the washroom or when emptying the cell bucket, but when she could, she asked them the same questions, and they promised they would ask those in their own cells.

Eugenia spoke in Russian to the first guard she encountered. He was surprised to hear good Russian spoken by a Pole, but met her entreaty with a stony silence and an irritated wave of his rifle in her face.

'We must keep trying, Mama,' said Halina, although she felt dispirited, 'we cannot give up.'

Eugenia took a deep breath and nodded. She knew she would never give up, but after a week of failure, she decided that she had to do something to stop herself brooding. That evening she took her poetry book out of her bag. If she read the poetry aloud, that would help distract her, as well as helping to pass the time. The evening prayers had comforted her, and now she would try to bring a little of Poland into the cell. She opened the book and started to recite. She spoke with passion and emotion, and managed to lose herself in each poem. After a blissful half hour of escape from her troubles, she put down the book and then realised everyone was looking intently at her.

'That was wonderful Eugenia,' said Maria, 'I almost forgot I was in prison.'

Eugenia put her book back in her bag. She had found a purpose. Something to help soften the terrible blow of losing Ola. She had brought a little comfort to herself by bringing a little comfort to others.

Fifteen

Ola aged 11
'Christina watched Ola... she was
such a pretty little thing. So like
her Irene.'

Ola, May 1940, Brest Children's Home

On the fifth Day, Ola decided she would stop crying. It did not make her feel better and at least half of the other children didn't cry, besides she was getting a sore throat and had to keep washing her handkerchief so she could use it when her nose ran. And of course she did not want to wet her pants again. That had been humiliating, as she sat in the back of the wagon taking her from the prison to this beastly place. She had cried so hard she did not even notice she had done it until she felt a horrible warm wetness on her seat. She wriggled uncomfortably at the memory and looked around, to take her mind off it.

The dining hall could hardly be called a hall, it was just a small room with a couple of long tables with forty or fifty children squashed together. The boy next to her jogged her elbow and she glared at him. 'Sorry,' he said and looked as if he would begin to cry. She put her spoon in the stuff that they had for breakfast. Some kind of cereal it was supposed to be, but there was hardly any milk and so it had to be eaten with water. The first spoonful was the worst, but she had to keep her strength up, as Mama would say, and at least it was better than that awful soup and bread they had in the fort.

A sharp pain stabbed her, but it was just the memory of Mama and Halina coming back. No, she was not going to cry again. She gripped her spoon hard until her knuckles were pure white and pinched her thigh under the table. That was better. Now she would not cry.

Christina watched Ola eating her breakfast. She was such a pretty little thing. So like her Irena. Christina was a plump, kindly woman in her fifties. Her husband and daughter had drowned in a boating accident and, alone and lonely, she had started working at the children's home twenty years earlier. When the Soviets took over, her experience made her valuable and she stayed on, reporting to the NKVD director. She did not like the way the Soviets treated everyone, but at least she was able to stay with the children who gave her so much comfort.

Until the invasion, the home had been an orphanage and only held children who had lost their parents, but now there were children who had been taken forcibly from their mothers, and that was something she found hard to accept. She had noticed Ola as soon as she arrived, as she reminded her of the daughter she had lost all those years ago. She was pleased that she appeared to be settling down a little and did not cry as often. Ola's mother was in prison as 'an enemy of the people', or so the Director had informed her. She smiled at Ola. Poor little thing. If only she could do more to help her.

Ola noticed Christina looking at her and thought she seemed nice. Christina had spoken to her once or twice since she arrived, but she had been too upset to respond. If she got the chance she would talk to her, she seemed so much nicer than the teachers who took her lessons. The lessons were dreadful. Nothing but talk about Stalin, whoever he was – she did not listen- and then they had to sings songs in Russian about the glorious Soviet leader. There was no way she would be top of the class when to do that she had to learn all that Stalin rubbish.

Anna, the girl who sat beside her in class, was quite kind to her. She had given her a hug when she was crying, or at least one of the many times she had been crying. She must stop crying. What would Papa think - an officer's daughter crying all the time!

'Are you feeling better now?' Anna was speaking.

'A bit. Thank you. Did I tell you, Anna, I had a doll by that name? We had to sell it though.' Anna was not quite sure what to make of that, but did not have to answer because the teacher came into the room.

That night, Ola stood looking out of the window. Yet another day of Stalin, Stalin, and Stalin, with a bit of mathematics and writing thrown in. There was some music but that seemed to be all about Stalin again. No art, no Polish, and the history lessons were full of lies about the glorious Soviets beating the Polish rats. She missed her mother so much it still hurt to think about her. As she looked out of the window, an idea came to her. She would escape!

She spoke to her friend about her idea next day, but Anna was not impressed. 'It is not too bad here. I have been here for ages and it is not too bad. We have food to eat and they are not cruel to us. I miss Mama, but where would I go to look for her if I escaped?'

Ola decided she would have to escape on her own, and she sat and plotted all through her lessons. She would mumble something when asked a question, having decided that pretending to be simple was a much better idea. Then they would not imagine her clever enough to escape. But first she needed a Plan.

Eugenia, Halina, May 1940, Brest Prison

Several weeks passed. Each day in the prison, they received the familiar bread, hot water and soup, but Halina was becoming used to the lack of food and did not feel hungry as often. The lack of activity affected her and she eagerly awaited the daily trip to the toilet, just for the short walk along the corridors. The other women in the cell told their stories, many being similar to theirs. Guides, who had promised to take them over the border, had betrayed some, but others were political prisoners. As Bella had said, there was an underground army, consisting of soldiers who had escaped capture, together with others who were determined to resist the invaders, using various methods including sabotage and subversion.

Halina watched her mother as she listened to the stories. It was such a relief that Mama seemed more like herself. She had been so frightened when she thought she had lost her mind. By comparison, even the lack of activity was just about bearable. She decided that she had to ask each day without fail, if anyone knew of a children's home nearby. That seemed to help Mama. It was disappointing that, so far, there had been no information, but at least it gave her something to do. It was difficult to decide what was worse, lack of food or boredom.

After about three weeks, a new prisoner came to their cell. She was a woman in her early twenties and spoke in very cultured tones. When the round of introductions was over, Halina sat beside her and asked the question she had asked many times before.

'Yes, I come from near Brest,' she answered, 'I think there is a children's home to the north of the city about five miles outside the city boundary. I think the Soviets have taken it over, but I am not sure.'

Eugenia felt great relief when she heard the answer to Halina's question. Perhaps her little Ola was there. She would redouble her efforts to speak to the guards.

Two days later, she had almost given up hope of receiving any kind of answer to her questions, when she noticed the young guard who had explained to her so gently that Ola could not stay in the cell with her. 'Do you know where they took my daughter?' she asked, 'Is it to the children's home north of Brest?'

The guard looked at her and for one dreadful moment, she thought he was not going to answer. 'It is true I have taken some children there,' he answered finally, 'and it is possible your daughter is there.'

Despite the vagueness of his answer, Eugenia was overjoyed. If she knew where Ola was, she would be able to worry a little less, and when the war was over, she would know where to look for her. She would keep asking the guards until she had news that was more definite.

However, she did not get the chance. Later that day, the cell door swung open and a Soviet guard shouted the name Korbinska.

After hastily collecting their belongings, Halina and Eugenia joined a large group outside the prison. They were loaded onto wagons and driven to a railway station. Halina was thankful she was moving again, but Eugenia was very apprehensive. She could just about cope with the conditions in Brest prison, but feared the unknown. Where were they going? Would things be better or worse? She had at last found out where Ola was, only to be moved away from her. It seemed as if she had lost her all over again.

On arriving at the station, Halina looked around for a train, but all she could see were large wooden trucks with high sides.

'Cattle trucks,' Eugenia whispered, remembering the awful sight in Luck, 'surely we are not going in them.'

They were. One by one, they climbed up the steep steps into the wagon and made their way inside. As they found their way to a corner, Halina remembered what she had been told about the cattle trucks by her mother.

'Mama,' she said, 'Are we being deported to Siberia?'

Eugenia put her arm around her, 'I think they would tell us if that was the case. From what I heard the guards saying, we are going to a prison in Russia.' Her ability to speak Russian may have made the NKVD suspicious in Luck, but here in the cattle truck it served her well.

There was a metal stove in the centre of the wagon with a chimney reaching up and out of the roof of the wagon. At each end there were planks arranged like shelves. Halina noticed there was a hole in the floor near one end of the wagon that she soon realised was the toilet arrangement. Using a bucket in front of the few women in the cell she had left had been embarrassing enough, but here she would have to squat in a carriage full of strangers. Just as she was wondering how she would cope, someone erected a barrier with some wood and a blanket. Thank goodness, that would be one less indignity to suffer.

It was nearly June and quite warm in the cattle truck. There were no windows, but there were several open grilles near the top of the truck. By sitting on one of the shelves at the end, Halina could just manage to see out. There were many people on the platform, some carrying bags, some without. Most were women and children and they were climbing into wagons further along the train. Where were they going? Why did they want to take her to Russia? The train started with a jerk and she felt a pang of fear. She was on her way to the unknown.

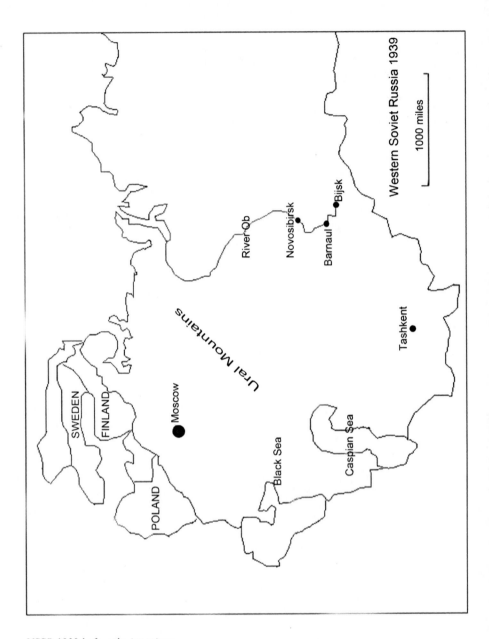

USSR 1939 before the invasions.

Sixteen

Eugenia, Halina, June 1940, Homel Prison

The journey took two days, with the train stopping at intervals to pick up more prisoners. Soup and bread was given to them each day, and water supplied regularly, but the journey was uncomfortable, hot and tiring. Eventually the train stopped again, but this time the door was opened wide. Several soldiers with rifles approached, and told them to get up and leave. Eugenia clambered out, stiff from several days without exercise and looked around. It was dark and gloomy, and a slight breeze was blowing. After the stuffy and sometimes very smelly truck, the air smelled wonderfully fresh. She sniffed the air. 'It is so balmy,' she said to Halina, 'even if it is Russian air.' It was dark, the station lit with oil lamps erected at intervals.

On the station platform, she caught sight of a sign that read Homel. They were in Russia, 'But near Moscow,' she added quickly, 'not in Siberia.' She had recovered a little from her deep depression at losing Ola, buoyed up with the hope that she would be able to find her again after the war.

They joined the line of prisoners, and walked along the dimly lit streets, stumbling now and then over cobbles in the road. Despite the difficulty of walking in darkness, Eugenia enjoyed the chance to smell fresh air and take the exercise denied her in prison. She was disappointed when finally they stopped, and entered an austere building with barbed wire-topped walls.

Before entering the cells, they were searched. Halina was quickly frisked and her bag searched, but Eugenia was subjected to a much longer ordeal. The guard took a long time passing his hands over her body carefully exploring each crevice. She held her breath and looked straight ahead, willing the experience to pass. At one point, she caught sight of the guard's face. There was nothing sexual in his expression, but another light altogether shone in his eye. He knew how upsetting she was finding the search and he was prolonging it deliberately to take his pleasure in her humiliation. Eugenia gritted her teeth. He would not have the satisfaction of seeing her cry.

Once moving again, they stopped in front of a metal gate which was unlocked, and which led to a corridor and yet another gate. Eventually a final gate opened and they entered a long corridor. A little light shone through a barred window at the end, and Eugenia could see several doors with metal grilles on either side. The guard opened one of the doors, and pushed her inside with Halina.

The cell was much smaller than the one they had left in Brest, but there was the same number of people inside. The walls were of dirty grey stone, full of cracks and covered here and there with stains. The door wall was solid for the bottom half, with bars set in the top half. The only air in the cell came through the bars and it was sour and dank. A light hanging from the ceiling cast dark shadows, which added to the nightmarish appearance of what Eugenia saw. There were no bunks, just a bare concrete floor on which lay half-naked women, tightly packed together. The women were filthy. There was a partly covered grating in the far side of the cell, and a thin stream of moonlight shone through, highlighting the dirt on the walls.

She looked around in horror. Dear God, what had they come to. Some of the women woke up and began shouting at them. They all spoke in Russian and were complaining that there was little enough room without more people coming. Despite that, they moved a little closer to each other so that there was a tiny space for them.

Eugenia lowered herself gingerly to the floor and pulled Halina beside her. 'Don't worry,' she said to Halina, 'I am sure we will not be here for long.' She did not believe it was true, but somehow she had to try to protect her daughter from the dreadful truth. The conditions were far worse than she could have imagined. She looked at the woman lying next to her. Her neighbour stank of sweat and other body odours that she did not want to think about too closely. Her hair was lank and greasy and it was obvious it had not been washed for some time. Eugenia tried to avoid physical contact, but the cramped conditions made it impossible. Surely there must be lice in these conditions.

She felt sick at the thought and remembered something Kazimierz had told her about lice, not long after she had married him. He had been very casual about the subject and had laughed at her disgust. Apparently, it was something all soldiers who had fought in wars talked about casually. What was it he had said? Three main types of lice? Head lice, which were quick to populate the hair, and hard to get rid of. Regular combing of the hair was required. The eggs would stick to the hair shaft and had to be pulled off. Then there were body lice. She swallowed down bile as she remembered what he had said about body lice. They lived between the skin and the clothes and multiplied rapidly. It was necessary to boil clothes if possible, as body lice carried typhus. She remembered he had been rather embarrassed when describing the third type. 'Spread by sexual contact,' he had mumbled, 'not that I have experience of it, of course Eugenia.'

She looked at her neighbour's filthy, ragged clothing and a slight movement caught her eye. No. It could not be lice. She had only just been thinking about them. It was just her imagination. But no. There it was again. This time it was not her imagination. It really was lice. The woman's clothing was covered in them. Eugenia turned her head away fighting the urge to vomit. She could not do that in here. She would not. It would make things unbearable for everyone. She closed her eyes and concentrated hard on praying. Dear God, please help me. Please help. The minutes crawled slowly by and gradually the urge passed.

As she looked across at the other women, even in the dim light she could see that they were equally filthy. Several started to scratch in their sleep. How could anyone sleep here? One woman in particular had rashes and weeping ulcers all over her body, even on the soles of her feet. That she was sure was syphilis.

Kazimierz had not told her about syphilis, but she had read about it in a medical book of her father's when she was twenty and about to get married. She had been looking for something about sex, as her mother had told her almost nothing about it, and had stumbled on the section on syphilis. She had been horrified and fascinated at the same time, but the dreadful pictures had stopped her reading further than the symptoms. The subject of syphilis was not one that came up in polite conversation, so her knowledge was only basic. Could she catch it just being close to the women? What if Halina caught it?

The feeling of sickness started to come again. She must think about something else. Ola. Dear sweet Ola. Thank God, she was not here as well. She could not bear it if Ola had to suffer these conditions. She was not sure that she could cope with the conditions herself.

She slept very little that night. Every hour or so, someone started pushing and wriggling and they all shifted a little or turned on their side to prevent getting an elbow in their ribs. After a while, they learned to turn together. Throughout the night, she could hear prisoners along the corridor shouting and arguing. Once or twice in a nearby cell, she could hear the screaming of a woman who seemed to have given in completely to despair.

To pass the time, she studied the women in her cell. They looked so rough and their language was so coarse, they could only be criminals. She had to try to create a positive bond with these women, awful as they looked, especially as several of them appeared capable of violence. She tried out some Russian phrases in her head. Thank God, she could speak Russian.

She drifted off to sleep then woke a few minutes later. Someone was using the toilet pail. It was the woman with the sores. At least she was next to the bucket and did not have to move anyone. Eugenia turned her head away but could not escape the onslaught of the dreadful smell from the bucket, whose contents had been disturbed. She felt sick again. Halina moved against her and her panic was replaced with concern for her. Whatever happened she must try to appear positive. Somehow, she must distract Halina. Perhaps with poetry. She thought of her favourite Polish poem of love and finally drifted off into sleep an hour before dawn.

In the morning, the guards brought them coarse black bread and hot water. 'Make it last,' said one of the women to Eugenia, 'that is all the bread you will get today.'

As they ate their bread, the women stared curiously at Eugenia and Halina. The contrast between them was stark. Despite their dirty clothes and their exhaustion, there was no doubt that Halina and Eugenia were cultured. It was shown in the quiet way they spoke to each other, the gentle smiles, the way in which they moved. They did not look as if they were in prison for the same crimes as themselves. The Russian women staring at the Polish couple had been arrested for stealing, prostitution and even murder. 'Why are you here?' asked one.

'We were arrested crossing the border,' explained Eugenia. She decided not say too much about her privileged background, which was so obviously different from that of her cellmates. She must try hard not to show any contempt for them. That could be dangerous. 'They took my daughter from me.' Speaking Russian had been the right decision. The women visibly became friendlier and started to say why they had been imprisoned.

'Five of us are here for stealing,' one of the younger women volunteered. She was not much older than Halina, but had a hard expression that told of a life of poverty and deprivation. 'Anna is in for murder. Who was it you murdered then, Anna?' she shouted. The woman she addressed turned to Eugenia, 'My lover of course, he was sleeping with someone else, and he deserved it. They were out to get me. The voices told me I had to kill him. They told me I had to.' Anna put her hands over her ears and crouched in the corner.

'The rest are prostitutes.'

'Hey, who are you calling a prostitute,' screamed the woman with the rashes that had so disgusted Eugenia the night before.

A guard appeared at the door and told them to get moving. For a moment, Eugenia felt terror. What would she have to suffer next? However, it was just the morning trip to the toilet and washroom.

'At last a chance to wash, Halina,' she said, forcing a smile. She could not wait to wash away all evidence of last night's contact with her cellmates.

Halina had been very sleepy when they had arrived the night before, and had somehow managed to sleep for a few hours. She had only become fully aware of her surroundings when she woke up. She stood in a queue with twenty-five women waiting for the toilet amid shouts of 'Hurry up in there!' from the others in the queue. Finally, it was her turn and she moved urgently through the door and shut it behind her.

She looked around in abject horror and only just managed to keep her breakfast down. The toilet was just a hole in the ground, but was a hole used by 100 women every day. The sight was disgusting. The area round the hole was caked in excrement and there were splashes all round the walls and on every bit of floor. She closed her eyes. It was so utterly revolting. How could she cope with this? She would have to try to think of something pleasant. Fields of flowers perhaps. But no flower was strong enough to blank out that awful stench. How dare the Soviets treat her like this!

The other women in the queue were shouting and hammering on the door for her to finish. Most of them were Russian. They could just wait. However, even defiance did not help her and when finally she opened the door she was in a state of shock and stood outside with her hands trembling.

'It gets cleaned every day,' said a sympathetic voice in Polish, 'and you do get used to it.'

Halina could not speak. If she said anything, she would start crying. She clenched her fists, anger building in her until her jaw ached from tension. Washing became even more vital now and she walked quickly into the washroom. Most of the women were completely naked with the exception of a few Polish women who modestly had retained some underwear.

She stood and looked in dismay at the small amount of water she had to wash in - little more than a cupful. How could she possibly clean herself with that!

'Be careful and don't splash it,' said Eugenia who was standing next to her.

Halina took the tiny piece of soap and rubbed it all over her skin using a small washcloth she had brought. Carefully she rinsed off the soap with some of the water. She must not show how upset she was. She did not want Mama to worry about her. She could not bear it if she broke down as she had in Brest prison.

As the morning wore on, she recovered a little from the first shock of their conditions, but another was to come. As she sat on the floor trying to sleep to pass the time, she felt a strange creeping sensation on her head. Eugenia combed through her hair to look.

'What is it?' she asked, expecting her to pull out a spider

'So sorry Halina,' she said, 'you have got lice'

Halina pulled back in disgust. 'Get them off,' she said, feeling sick.

Eugenia looked at her and held her hand. 'Halina, we have been very lucky to escape so far,' she said, stroking her face, 'but there is no avoiding them. We do not have enough water or enough soap, and even if we washed all day we would probably catch them from the other women,' she tilted her head towards their fellow prisoners, 'I have a few too, I think,' she added. Hopefully, Halina had not detected the disgust in her voice or noticed that her hand was shaking.

Halina watched the other women more closely, and every now and then, she saw them pick something off their clothes and squash it. She realised with horror that the ritual had been going on without her noticing. She seemed to itch all over and every speck on her clothes made her panic. 'What do I do, Mama? How can I get rid of them?'

Eugenia brought out her comb. 'I will comb through your hair night and morning and remove anything I find. Then we will wash our clothes twice a day.' Halina moved closer and Eugenia searched carefully through each strand of her daughter's hair. What did lice look like? How was she to know if she had found one? Something moved across the comb. She would have to squash it. She would have to touch that thing and squash it. 'That's one, Halina. I don't think there are many more. We will soon be finished.' There was no escape. She would just have to grab it. She held her breath and grabbed the parasite, which squashed easily in her fingers. She shuddered with revulsion. How could Kazimierz be so casual about them.

'That's them all, Halina. Now can you do the same for me? Just think of them as Soviet lice. That will help.'

Halina reluctantly took the comb and quickly looked through her mother's hair, fighting the disgust that she did not attempt to hide. How would she cope if they spread to her clothes?

The Russian prisoners had been watching the operation with interest and some amusement. 'It's only lice dear,' one of the older women said, 'They are always around. They won't harm you.'

Halina tried to hide her feelings. If these Russian women could cope, she must be able to. However, it was several days before she could bring herself to squash them. By then she had no choice. Body lice had started to make their appearance.

Eugenia killed the first of the invaders. By now, she was inured to the tiny crunch between her fingertips. She would not let them win. But how could she keep them at bay? Thank goodness it was summer, and warm. That way she and Halina could wear the light clothing they had with them and wash it every day. The fight would keep her occupied and take her mind off the hellish conditions. Once she gave up the fight to keep clean, she would give up the fight altogether. She would not do that. A guard appeared with the evening soup. A distraction from the vermin, but the food was so awful she was not sure it was a welcome one.

Seventeen

Eugenia, Halina, June 1940, Homel Prison

The soup in her bowl was looking back at her. She was sure of it. Halina sighed and dunked her crust of black bread in. It made no difference. It still tasted awful. The food was bad enough in Brest, but at least the soup was usually drinkable and the bread was not this awful black stuff. And of course there was the toilet – that was a hundred times worse here. She shuddered as she remembered the filth and the smell. She would be visiting it every day she was here, so she would have to get used to it. She looked at Eugenia. At least Mama seemed to have recovered from the initial shock of the conditions.

She looked at the soup again. She felt sick every time she thought of that toilet, but she was so hungry, she could not help but drink the soup, despite how disgusting it looked. She would have to imagine it was delicious and tasty and then perhaps she would not worry what the strange lumpy bits were. The bits that seemed to look back at her. They looked like animal eyes. She remembered what a girl in the next cell had told her about the bread. That sometimes there were cockroaches cooked in it. She grimaced. Some extra protein perhaps? She felt sick again at the thought. However, the overwhelming sensation was hunger. And there would be nothing else until the next day.

Later that week, a guard came to tell the prisoners that they could volunteer to wash the floors and Halina agreed with enthusiasm. Washing meant access to water, and she would have the opportunity to save tiny flakes of soap. That would help with the impossible task of keeping clean. There was also the possibility she would be given a little more food for doing the work. Before she started on the corridors, she filled the bucket and scrubbed every corner of the cell. Too bad if the other women in the cell complained – they would appreciate the improved hygiene soon enough. Eugenia talked to the women in the cell and they cooperated, grudgingly at first, but gradually with good grace. Some of them even started making more effort to keep clean.

Once Halina was occupied with washing floors, Eugenia no longer had the distraction of worrying about her daughter, and as she felt depression starting to creep over her, she realised that she had to work out a strategy for coping with the prison conditions. She had to treat it like a war. Fight or surrender completely to despair. Some of the Resistance girls in Brest prison had told her of their training in survival, and she tried to recall their advice.

She was not being tortured or beaten, so she had to concentrate on developing mental strength. It sounded straightforward, but the dirt, the overcrowding and the dreadful food were bad enough, without the constant hunger and the anguish at what she had lost, so how could she keep mentally strong? Having nothing to do all day left her with too much time to brood on her misfortunes, and she could not stop herself from worrying about what would come after prison.

She pushed her hair from her face and tried to stop her hands from shaking. She had to do something. Perhaps if she divided each day into tasks, then she could concentrate on each small part of the day at a time, and forget the rest. Waking up each morning and contemplating a whole day at a time was terrifying.

They had bread and water early in the morning, so that could be the first section. Going to the toilet and washroom was the second part. She shuddered as she recalled the dreadful conditions in the toilet. But she had washing afterwards, and however inadequate the conditions, that was a part to look forward to. In addition, the walk to the toilet and back was a pleasure. After the washroom, she had a louse hunting session with Halina. She must try to think positively about that. Somehow, she had to think of it as removing lice and getting clean, instead of just being horrified at their presence. If Halina washed the cell in the morning, she could concentrate on picking over their clothes, looking for the parasites that had escaped destruction. Eugenia swallowed hard. She still found it difficult to cope with lice and the thought of endless days fighting parasites still made her feel sick. However, she had to try. Think of each louse as a Soviet soldier.

Lunchtime was something to look forward to, even though the food was almost inedible, but the long afternoon was a problem. She looked at her cellmates. They might be Russian criminals, but they had proved to be quite friendly, so perhaps she should reserve the afternoons for talking to them. If the less aggressive guards were on duty, she also would be able to talk to the Polish women in the neighbouring cells. Listening to the stories of other people would take her mind off her own problems a little.

The evening meal was another section, followed by toilet, washroom and a second louse hunt. The evenings were perhaps the easiest part of the day to plan. That was when she recited to Halina and lost herself in her poetry. For a few brief moments, she could almost imagine herself somewhere else. Then came night. A long period of prayer helped her sleep, and now that she could sleep for some of the night, she could dream herself into another world. Sleep was her only escape. Even if that was all she had to look forward to, it was better than nothing.

As Eugenia continued to plan her day, she found that she felt a little calmer. The panic, which she feared would never leave her, abated a little. Perhaps she really had found the solution to creating mental strength: compartmentalise her day and think of something to look forward to, however brief and short-lived. She had to try to value every moment of relief from worry. She picked up the damp clothes hung from the cell bars. It was morning and she had to carry out the louse hunt.

Each day Halina ventured a little further to wash floors. The guards generally took no notice of her as long as she had a bucket and brush in her hand. In her forays she met other Polish prisoners, several about her own age, and used the opportunity to talk to them, when the guards allowed, gaining a little comfort from the kinship.

A few weeks after her arrival, she had explored the corridors nearest to her and when she found another gate open, she walked a little further. Two guards came towards her so she hurriedly got to her knees and started scrubbing. 'Scrub hard, Polish cow,' one shouted and his colleague laughed. She ground her teeth together and scrubbed a little harder. She would just imagine those Soviet faces were underneath the bristles of the brush.

Once the soldiers had gone she stood up and was about to turn and go back the way she had come when she saw a young man coming down some steps. He was obviously a prisoner, his dirty clothes and thin face giving that away, and she said 'Hello,' tentatively.

'You are Polish,' he said, coming towards her, 'I am Polish too. My name is Witold.'

He was tall with black hair and as Halina looked up at him, she noticed his eyes were a dark, liquid brown. He smiled and she felt a faint flush come over her. But it did not matter if she blushed, he would realise she was attracted to him and she would not have to say so. She smiled back and started to introduce herself and to talk about her experiences. Witold said that he had been arrested for crossing the border. 'I think we are held here until they are ready to sentence us,' he added.

She felt a little dazed as he continued to talk. What was it he was saying? He had such beautiful dark eyes and they seemed to hold so much emotion.

Eventually he had to leave, 'I have been to deliver a message,' he said, 'I cannot stay any longer – if they catch me here it will not be good. I hope I will see you again Halina.' And he was gone.

She picked up her bucket. He was so handsome, and he seemed to find her attractive too. Who cared about lice, hunger, and dirt if she could see Witold again. It was such luck that she had gone to that corridor. She would go there each day and perhaps see him again

'Halina, are you all right? What has happened?'

Halina realised with a start that not only was she back at the cell, she had also dropped the bucket off. She had not remembered doing it. As she recounted her romantic interlude, Halina was gratified to hear the musical sound of her mother's laughter, a sound she had not heard for such a long time.

'Only you could find love in a prison, Halina!'

Each day she could, Halina travelled to the end of the corridors hoping to find Witold. The search was something she looked forward to and helped take her mind off the squalid surroundings. Each afternoon she returned disappointed, but each morning she set off again with fresh hope. In turn, Eugenia took pleasure in the fact that her daughter had found something positive to hold on to, and found that her own mood was a little lighter as well.

After several weeks, Halina was beginning to think she would never see Witold again, when she heard footsteps coming from the stairs where she had first seen him. It might be Witold! She hurried to the corner but stopped short. There was a strange whimpering sound. She felt her skin crawl. It was such an unearthly sound. A sound she had never heard before. The whimpering became louder, and she saw two guards coming down the steps supporting something between them.

As they approached, she saw that they were supporting a man, and that he was the source of the whimpering. Was that really a man? And why was he making that awful sound? She stood fixed to the spot and saw that the man had been savagely beaten. His eyes were closed, swollen and purple and his body was covered in blood. My God, what had happened to Witold? What had they done to him? Halina suddenly felt ice cold and her hands started shaking. She could not wait to see any more. She must go back to the cell and away from the dreadful sight.

She turned and ran quickly back to familiar ground. The water bucket splashed filthy water over her legs, but she hardly noticed. She dropped the bucket and ran into the safety of her cell where she sat in a corner. She must not be sick. If she breathed deeply and thought about something else, she would be fine. What had they done to you Witold? Just take deep breaths and breathe slowly. Eventually her heart rate slowed and she felt a little better.

She lay on the floor that night fighting sleep. If she slept, she might see that awful sight again. She might hear that dreadful sound. She put her fingers in her ears and tried to think beautiful thoughts, but she might never be able to think of love and those handsome dark eyes again, without thinking of torture, beatings and death. It was three days before she recalled that the man she had seen had fair hair. It had not been Witold.

Eighteen

Janina, June 1940, Warsaw

When the last of her pupils had left, Janina Korbinska had been quite upset. Her school had been a great joy to her before the war, but with the occupation, few local people could afford her fees and she had been forced to close the school. Now some months on, she was contemplating trying to start up again, but knew it would mean massive interference from the German occupiers. A tall, thin woman in her fifties, Janina had lost her fiancé in the First War and had never married. This was due in some part to the fact that her fiancé had encouraged Kazimierz to join the army, and Kazimierz' father had blamed her when he had run away to enlist. She did not miss a husband, but did regret not having children, and when she had graduated from Warsaw University, she had starting teaching and later opened her own school. That way she had the company of other people's children.

'I am off to bed, dear,' her aunt called out as she closed the door behind her. Mrs Korbinska had been fortunate in that her grand house had suffered little during the bombing and the German occupation, but was less fortunate when they decided to commandeer the top two floors. She had been allowed to stay on, but felt vulnerable in a house full of Germans, and had come to stay with Janina.

Janina woke from her reverie to say goodnight, then poured herself a glass of wine and sat looking at the fire. She still had a few bottles left and drank the contents of them sparingly, but tonight she felt like a treat. She was trying to decide whether to finish off the bottle or save it for another night when she heard a knock at the door. She jumped up nervously. A knock at the door could mean many things, most bad, but this was not the loud insistent banging of the Gestapo, rather it was quiet and hesitant. She opened the door, and standing on the doorstep was a young girl who looked about nineteen.

'Miss Korbinska, I have a letter for you.' There was something about the girl that Janina trusted immediately, and she invited her in. She took the girl into the living room, opened the letter and read it in dismay.

My Dear Janina,
Today I have had some very bad news. Eugenia and the girls have been arrested. They were trying to cross the River Bug into German-occupied Poland on their way to Warsaw. Unfortunately, they did not succeed and were taken to Brest. Titov has been trying to find out what has happened to them, but it is difficult to get news. He did say that prisoners are usually taken to Brest prison and then to Russia. Sometimes young girls of Ola's age are taken to the children's home in Brest, but he is not sure if that will be the case with Ola. It is possible they will all be deported to Russia. Titov only received the information in May, some weeks after Eugenia left here, and he says it can take several weeks for the couriers to bring messages, so I do not know if they are still in Brest or have moved on.
I am sorry to bring such bad news. I know that Kazimierz' mother will be upset. Titov will not be able to do anything himself as he is involved in other activities,

but he says the courier who brings the message may be able to help.
All my love,
Barbara

'How did you get the letter,' Janina asked the girl, who simply shrugged and smiled. 'Do you know anyone who could help me find out what has happened? If Ola is in the children's home in Brest, could you find her and bring her here?' she continued, 'I assume you know what is in the letter.'

The girl smiled again, 'I cannot say much, you understand, but there are people who can help. Crossing the border into Soviet-occupied Poland is dangerous, but it is possible.'

'I can pay. I assume the Resistance will always welcome money for its work.'

The girl smiled again, 'I will ask if there is someone free,' she said.

Three weeks later, in early July, Aniela, a woman in her early twenties, was on her way to Brest with forged papers, a letter from Janina and photographs of Eugenia, Halina and Ola. She was a courier who had crossed into Soviet-occupied Poland on several occasions, although each trip seemed more difficult and dangerous than the last. Travelling in German-occupied Poland on her own was relatively straightforward, as she knew one of the railwaymen who worked with the Resistance, and he was able to get hold of tickets and passes for her. She could use several safe houses on the way. Travelling in Soviet-occupied Poland however, was becoming more difficult, as several people who had helped her in the past had been arrested, but she was confident she could travel undetected.

Ola, June 1940, Brest Children's Home

Many weeks had passed and still Ola had no plan. She remembered something her father had said to the effect that planning took a long time. She must treat it like a military campaign. That was another phrase of her father's and she assumed it just meant a big plan. Big plans needed lots of time.

The first breakthrough came during a geography lesson. Not that it was what Ola called geography. It consisted of looking at a large map showing what she knew as eastern Poland, but what she was told was now Soviet territory. There in the middle was a very large splodge showing Brest, and a tinier cross where the children's home was. However, it was something else that caught Ola's eye. A small cross depicting a village. The village had a name she recognised. Kurnica. The name suddenly appeared larger than it was and in her imagination shot out a beam of light towards her. She was so shocked that she jumped, causing the teacher to look closely at her. Ola just smiled her 'simple' smile and the teacher sighed and returned to the map.

Kurnica. That was near where Uncle Jan lived! Ola thought the words but they were so loud in her head she was worried that she had said them aloud. But no, no one was looking. The family had last visited Uncle Jan and Auntie Paulina when she was five and she did not remember it much, but every birthday and Christmas, a present came from them. She was used to writing thank you letters and addressing them to Kurnica and could even remember the name of the small estate where they lived. Why on earth had she not thought of him before! She had not realised he was so near.

She started listening intently to the teacher as he described scales on the map to the class. How far was Kurnica from where she was? She could not ask that, but she noticed that the children's home was about twice the distance from Kurnica as it was from the outskirts of Brest, but in the opposite direction. After a few calculations in her head, she decided that the village was about ten miles from where she was. She could walk that easily. In a few days, at any rate.

Stage one of The Plan - where to go after escaping - was now complete. Stage two was the escape itself and that would be difficult. They were not usually supervised, but on the rare occasions they ventured outside the garden walls, they were closely monitored. And of course the walls were closed by locked gates. Some deep thinking was required.

Ola could not sleep that night. She was so excited about discovering how near she was to Uncle Jan that The Plan kept whirling in and out of her head. She had slept lightly and was now awake very early. She got up and went to the window. There was a faint light in the sky so she decided it must be about five in the morning. As she looked, she saw a porter walk towards the gate in the wall with a key. He opened the gate, wedged it with a stone and went outside. A few minutes later, he came in carrying a sack, followed by a man carrying another. The procedure was repeated several times before the two emerged from the kitchen, and the porter locked the gate after the delivery driver had gone. A way to escape already! Ola could hardly believe her luck.

Over the next two weeks, she watched at her window in the early morning. Deliveries came each Monday and Thursday. Each time the gate was wedged open, and each time the driver stayed in the kitchen for about ten minutes after the last trip. There were several bushes in the garden that she could hide behind.

She swapped places with Anna so she was on dishwashing duty, but at that stage, she had decided it better not to tell anyone of her plans, not even Anna. Once in the kitchen, she looked for places where she could hide, but every hiding place had one drawback – she would have to cross open floor and would certainly be seen by the porter and the driver. She stood for some time next to the sink, unaware that Christina, the Polish woman who worked there, was watching her.

'Is there a problem my dear? You can trust me,' said Christina as if she had read Ola's thoughts.

Ola thought for a minute and deciding that Christina was one person she could trust, told her about The Plan. Christina was quiet for a few moments then said, 'I can help you my dear. I can get some food and water for you to take, and can distract the porter and the driver so you can escape. All I have to do is offer them some breakfast, and they would not notice if a bull came into the room. I know someone who lives not far from here and her husband might be able to take you to your relatives.'

Ola was exultant, and a week later was ready for stage two of The Plan. She had to get up before five, but that was difficult as there were no clocks or watches in the dormitory, so she aimed to go downstairs the night before, when she thought everyone was in bed and it was quiet. That way she could wait in the kitchen in her hiding place. She lay in bed for several hours until she was sure it was safe, and then crept out to get dressed and finish packing her bag. She had partially packed it in a quiet moment, and just had to add her nightclothes.

Once dressed, she carefully opened the door. Christina had stolen some oil from the kitchen for the squeaky hinges, and the door was mercifully quiet. The kitchen was along a corridor and down some stairs. The stairs creaked at each step and by the time she reached the bottom, she could hardly hear for the sound of her heart beating. An easy trip into the kitchen, a squash into her hiding place behind a chest and she was ready.

Luck was with her and everything went smoothly. Christina came down about half an hour before the porter, and gave her food and water for her bag. She told Ola that her friend lived five miles along the road and had drawn a map for her. 'She lives in a small wooden cottage on its own set back from the road,' she instructed Ola, 'Show her the map and she will know who you are.'

The porter came down at five am, opened the back door and the gate. As he came back with the driver after the second load, Christina offered them breakfast and they moved to the opposite corner of the kitchen. Ola was able to cross the floor, walk out the door and then duck behind her chosen bush. She sidled up behind the shrubbery towards the gate, and while both men were still in the kitchen, she ran out of the gate in the direction of Kurnica, keeping the freshly rising sun on her right side.

Stage three – after the escape - proved much more difficult than Ola had imagined. She looked at Christina's map many times, but it was not very detailed and she had not taken account of turns and twists and ups and downs in the road. The sun was up and she was fully exposed. She had planned to duck into roadside bushes each time she heard a motor cycle or wagon, but they were more frequent than she had expected. As noon approached it became very hot, and she became very thirsty. The water she had brought was soon gone and she started to worry. She had been walking for hours and was afraid she might have missed the house Christina described.

A long convoy of lorries came towards her and she sat under a tree while they drove past. She looked around her and noticed a small wooden house behind her, about fifty yards from the road. Perhaps this was the house. She walked up to the windows and looked in. On the wall, she could see a crucifix and other signs to show that it was a Polish home. She walked round to the back of the house and found a woman digging in the garden. She smiled when she saw Ola.

'Hello dear, can I help you?'

Ola showed her the map and hoped against hope this was Christina's friend. Her luck held. The woman smiled at her again and said, 'You are the girl Christina told me about.'

After a drink and biscuit sitting in a tiny kitchen in the wooden house, Ola told her story to the woman who she found out was called Eva. 'Would you believe it,' Eva said, 'I was born near Kurnica. I know the estate you describe. My husband delivers wood and he will take you in his wagon when he comes home this evening.' Six hours later, Ola was sitting in a much larger kitchen with a surprised and delighted Uncle Jan and Auntie Paulina. She was feeling very sleepy after her escape and having eaten a delicious meal. She smiled to herself as her aunt took her upstairs and showed her the little room that was to be hers. The Plan had worked and she was once again the cleverest girl in the class.

Nineteen

Eugenia, Halina, August 1940, Homel Prison

After two months in the prison had passed, a guard came to the cell, called out the name Korbinska, and told Eugenia and Halina they had to go with him.

With some nervousness, they followed the guard to a room containing a large table at which sat two soldiers. Eventually they realised this was a 'court' and they were to be sentenced for the terrible crime of trying to cross a Soviet border.

'And when was the trial!' Halina exclaimed to her mother.

The men rambled on with the couple only understanding a few words, but the sentence was clearly pronounced. For Eugenia, there would be five years in a labour camp for adults, for being of the officer class and trying to cross the Soviet border. For the same 'crimes', Halina was awarded five years in a labour camp for twelve to eighteen year olds.

Halina looked at the soldier who had pronounced her sentence and she laughed loudly at him. This was not the response he expected, and he looked at her in puzzlement, 'Why are you laughing?'

Halina lifted her chin, looked down her nose at the seated official and mustered as much contempt as she could.

'I will not stay five years with you people!'

Eugenia did not know whether to be proud or fearful of Halina's spirit, but she was shocked when the sentence made it clear that she would be separated from her only remaining daughter. They had just a few hours together before Halina was escorted out of the prison leaving her mother behind. 'We will meet again soon I am sure,' she whispered. 'Never give up hope.'

Halina gritted her teeth and returned the smile. 'I am sure too,' she said. Inside she was screaming, 'Don't let them take me Mama', much as Ola had done. However, it would not stop them and it would just make Mama even more upset. She looked so distraught and if she broke down as she had when Ola had been taken, it would be unbearable. She had to try not to cry out. She had to try to force out a smile. She did not quite manage to remain calm and one tear escaped from its prison and rolled to freedom down her cheek. Perhaps Mama had not noticed.

Halina, August 1940, Soviet Russia

As the guards took her further away from Eugenia, Halina's fear increased. She had managed to adjust to most things with Mama to help her, but what would she do on her own? She would have no one to comfort her, no one to love her, no one to recite to her. All she knew of Russia was dirt, hunger, degradation and cruelty. Now she had to cope alone without protection. She wiped away some tears. At least she had told those soldiers at the court what she thought of them. She had not given them the satisfaction of seeing her cry.

She recalled how close her mother had been to losing her mind when Ola had been taken from her. Would she be able to cope now that her other daughter had been separated from her? This time she would not be there to shake Mama out of her despair. When she left, she turned back, she tried to smile, tried to show her that she would be fine, that there was no reason to worry. But she could no longer help Mama. She just had to try to look after herself.

As she left the gates of the prison, four Soviet girls joined her with another guard. This time they were not bundled into a wagon, but were made to walk through the streets towards the station. Some people shouted things, but Halina was so wrapped up in her unhappiness that she did not register what they were saying. Her little bag did not have much in it, as she had so few possessions, but after a while, it started to hurt her arm and she had to keep changing hands.

The first time, she stopped and put it down on the ground first, but the guard shouted at her to get going. He looked as if he was ready to hit her with his rifle butt, so she picked the bag up quickly in her other hand and scuttled forward to catch up with the others. After that, she became adept at changing hands while still walking. When they arrived at the station, they entered a third class carriage with the windows partially boarded up. At least this time it was not a cattle truck.

The train rushed on for several hours, and as night drew in they stopped at a station and the guards hustled her, and the four Soviet girls who had boarded the train with her, out of the carriage and onto the station platform. They lined up carrying their belongings and marched along a street towards the police station. The guards were obviously going somewhere for the night and wanted the prisoners safely locked up while they slept.

The police guards did not look too pleased to see them, but bundled them into a cell and even provided them with a small quantity of bread each and some soup. Halina sat clutching her small bundle of possessions, her mouth watering. She felt so hungry. All she could think about was food. As long as she had food, she could bear not being with Mama. The soup was thick and tasty, quite luxurious compared to the thin prison gruel they had left behind. She put the empty bowl down and finished the bread, but was unable to stop some tears from rolling down her face. Now she was not as hungry, her fear had returned.

'Why do you cry,' said a voice.

Halina look around and for the first time noticed an old woman in the cell with her. She was dressed in black, with rags wrapped round her feet and looked none too clean. There was a dirty coloured scarf on her head with contrasted strangely with the dark clothes. She looked like a gypsy woman.

'My mother has gone to a labour camp in Siberia and I am going somewhere else. I do not know if I will see her again.'

'Do not cry,' she said, 'You will see your mother again.'

Halina look at her more closely, noticing the deep lines etched on her face and the kindly brown eyes. She seemed so confident, but how could she know about her mother?

'You will see your mother again,' the old woman repeated.

Halina felt her fear receding a little. The old woman seemed to know so much. Surely a gypsy woman could not be wrong?

That night was uncomfortable as she lay on the hard stone floor, but there was plenty of room in the cell, unlike the previous jail, so she managed to sleep a little. She woke in the morning feeling quite cheerful, and then remembered where she was and that she was alone. Tears started to well up. She recalled the prediction of the gypsy woman who was looking at her again. She quickly blinked away the tears and smiled weakly at her. The old woman nodded her head but said nothing more.

Halina was given bread and a kind of tea for breakfast and allowed to use the toilet. It was little more than a hole in the ground, but was reasonably clean. Compared to the prison she had left, it was positively sparkling.

The guards returned soon after they had eaten and once more, they were lined up and marched along the street. There was another train waiting in the station, and as soon as they had boarded, it took off. The Soviet girls sat opposite Halina, and she was aware that they were looking at her. She was wearing her Polish school uniform that had spent much of its time wrapped in her bag in the prison, and so was clean if rather wrinkled. It was made of a good woollen cloth, which she could see was much better quality than the dirty rather ragged clothes they wore. Halina smiled at them, but she was in no mood for conversation. She knew very little Russian so far and making herself understood would have been too difficult. She looked out of the small window. She would ignore their envious stares. She really did not care what they thought. Despite everything, she was starting to feel curious about her destination. It could be as bad as the prison she had just left, but she had survived that. How bad could things really be?

Eugenia, August 1940, Homel Prison

As she watched Halina leave, Eugenia was in despair. First one and now both daughters had been taken from her. The other women who watched with her, tried to comfort her, but she scarcely heard them. She returned to her cell and sat down, fighting the emotions that threatened to overwhelm her. Now she had nothing left. Her husband had gone, she had lost her home, her possessions, her way of life and now both her daughters. Was there any point in going on? She had been so cheered by discovering Ola was likely to be in a children's home in Brest. Had she been deluding herself? She suddenly felt faint and rested her head on her knees. If she went to Siberia, she might never see them again.

After a few minutes, she reached into her bag to take out her precious photographs of Ola and Halina, wrapped in Ola's socks. She held the socks to her cheek, and recalled the weeks she and Halina had spent trying to find out where Ola had been taken. Halina had been so upset at her reaction to losing Ola, and she could sense the same feelings waiting in the wings. However, if she gave in to her despair now, she knew she would never recover from it. Several women in the prison had been unable to cope with the terrible changes in their circumstances. One in particular had spent her days crouched in a corner crying and wailing, unable to eat or drink. The woman had died after four weeks and she could still remember the awful sound of her cries. What would happen to Ola and Halina when the war was over if she was not around? What if Kazimierz had been killed? There might be no one for them.

Eugenia sat in the dim light with the socks in one hand and the photographs in the other. She could not give up. She had to believe that God would help her. She had to believe that the war would end and she would see her children again. She could not give up hope and be destroyed by grief, as others had been. She replaced the socks and the photographs and brought out her ermine collar.

The collar was her reminder of the life she once had, but there was also a practical value, as sewn into the lining was last of the money she had left from selling her jewellery in Luck. She had kept it folded in her bag ever since her capture and had only occasionally looked at it. As she stroked the soft fur, it rekindled her determination to get through her difficulties. It reminded her of what she must strive to have once more.

She started to pray with a fierce energy and eventually felt calmer. There was a deep pain in her chest and she still felt depressed, lonely and fearful. However, there was a tiny flame of hope.

A few days later, she was once more in a cattle truck, this time bound for Siberia and the unknown. The flame still flickered within her.

Twenty

Eugenia, August 1940, Soviet Russia

As the train speeded up, the trucks swung about so much that if she stood up, she was thrown against the walls. Eugenia had no alternative but to sit down. She placed her bag between herself and the floor, so that she did not have to sit directly on the filthy surface. The old woman she sat next to looked at her.

'Is that all they let you bring?' she asked.

'It was all I had,' Eugenia replied, 'I was trying to cross the border when I was arrested so I had only a small bag.'

'They gave us twenty minutes to pack. Twenty minutes to pack everything we had. They hammered on the door at one in the morning and told us to get ready to go, and to bring warm clothes.' The old woman shook her head, 'We heard of others being deported but hoped they had missed us. My daughter had the good sense to pack food and water, but I think it went in another coach. Siberia they said. What is the point of taking an old woman to Siberia? I will not be able to work.'

'Did they say you would be going to a labour camp?' Eugenia gathered that the woman was a deportee and had not spent time in prison as she had.

'No, just that we would be going somewhere cold. However, I know about labour camps as the Tsar sent my brother there in 1906. Never saw him again.' The woman looked at Eugenia. 'I am not afraid. I am old and have a weak heart, so I expect death soon enough. However, I worry about my daughter and her children. We were separated at the station and I do not know which coach they are in. We have been travelling a week. They give us hardly any food or water. We will be travelling for weeks more, and in this heat.'

Eugenia wiped the sweat from her forehead. It was stifling. There were sixty people crammed in the truck, which was being heated by the sun. The only ventilation was by way of several small grilles. The truck was similar to the one in which she had travelled from Brest to Homel, but on that journey there had been fewer people and they had sufficient water and food. It was now early August, and the summer sun was heating the truck unbearably. But she had survived so much already. What could be worse than the conditions in Homel prison?

She looked at the other occupants who were obviously shocked and terrified, and had not had time to adjust mentally, before being thrust into hell. She would conserve her strength and try to ignore the physical surroundings. She reminded herself that the most important thing was to keep strong mentally and then she could deal with the rest. She turned her head to look at her neighbour. The old woman next to her was unwell and might need comfort. She would talk to her and take her mind off her own problems.

Each day for ten days as they travelled, Eugenia sat and listened to the old woman's wet breathing as her heart struggled to cope with heat and dehydration. At night, once or twice, she woke when the ragged sound stopped, only to find that it started again, uneven and laboured. She woke up one more night to the silent sound, but this time breathing did not begin again. She stroked the woman's face, which was cold and still. At least the old woman's suffering was over. She would support the woman's weight against the swaying movement of the train until the next time they stopped. It would give her some dignity.

After several hours of daylight, the train stopped, the doors opened and water appeared, with the miracle of soup and bread at the same time. As the guard entered, the old woman's body slumped over onto his foot and he muttered a curse before calling for help. Despite remembering the scene at Luck station, Eugenia hoped for some gentleness and care, but the guards' action shocked even her. They picked up the body and threw it down the side of the embankment where it bounced and rolled before coming to a halt. Just a bundle of coloured rags with an arm outstretched, like an abandoned marionette. Those in the carriage who witnessed the atrocity were silent and grey-faced, until someone started a prayer that many in the carriage joined. Then the doors slammed shut and once more the train started into motion.

When the sun had set, there was very little light inside the truck, and it quickly became pitch dark, any stray light being eagerly absorbed by those near the grilles. Eugenia took deep breaths to stop her heart from pounding. When there was no moon, as now, the dark seemed solid and enveloping. Young children were becoming frightened and she could hear their cries echoing round the truck. As the night became darker, there was a sense of rising panic, everyone fearing having nightmares of the day's events.

Eugenia remembered the small poetry book that she had read aloud to Halina in prison. Everyone had told her how much her reciting had helped, by giving a respite, however brief, from the horror. She knew almost every verse by heart, and started to recite poems of Poland, of love lost, of love found. Slowly, the sounds of panic abated. All that could be heard was the rattling of the trucks and the humming of the rails, in tune with Eugenia's voice, as it rose and fell, and pushed back the suffocating, black velvet of night.

Ola, August 1940, Kurnica

Ola sat in the garden of her uncle's house looking at the sky. Perhaps Mama and Halina could see the sky. Or were they still shut in that prison? She shivered at the memory of being taken from her mother. Try as she might, she could not forget that terrible event and some nights she woke up screaming, 'Don't let them take me, Mama.' Auntie Paulina was very kind and would come in and comfort her, but it always took her some time to go back to sleep, for fear of the nightmares returning. She looked towards the house. Uncle Jan was in earnest discussion with a man who Auntie Paulina said used to work for them. Whatever they were talking about, it looked very important.

That evening as they sat round the table, Ola could sense that her uncle and aunt were worried. She saw the same look on their faces that Mama had when they had been arrested. It was quite frightening. 'Uncle Jan,' she ventured, 'do you think we will be deported or is it safe here?'

Her uncle looked at her and smiled, 'I don't think so Ola.' Ola was not convinced by his reply and was about to ask whether he meant they would not be deported or would not be safe, when there was a knock at the door. Her aunt got up and came back with a woman who did not look much older than Halina.

'Ola,' said the woman, 'I have come from your aunt Janina in Warsaw. She would like you to go and stay with her and your Granny.'

Paulina and Jan looked with astonishment at the woman, who said her name was Aniela. 'How on earth did you get across the border?' Jan asked.

Aniela smiled and said nothing. She put her hand in her pocket and drew out the letter from Janina, together with the photographs she had been given. 'I have been trying to find out where Ola's mother and sister have been taken.' She looked at Jan and Paulina. 'I am afraid it looks as if they have been sent to Russia, possibly to prison, possible to Siberia, we do not know.'

Paulina sat down with her hand to her mouth. It was as she had feared. Living near Brest, they managed to get news easily and they knew that the prisoners in Brest did not stay long. 'How did you know Ola was here?' she asked Aniela.

'I have.....,' Aniela hesitated, '...contacts here who put me in touch with a woman at the children's home near Brest. Most of the children separated from their parents end up there for a time.'

'Christina!' Ola interrupted.

'Yes,' Aniela nodded at Ola, 'She knew Ola had come here and gave me the address. Once she realised who I was, that is.'

Jan spoke to Ola, 'Go up and collect your things, Ola. We love having you here, but it will be better for you to go to your aunt.' Ola did as she was told, but wondered why Uncle Jan was so keen for her to leave.

While Ola was packing her bag for what seemed to her to be the umpteenth time, Jan spoke to Aniela. 'I am so glad you have come. It is becoming very dangerous here. I was talking today to someone who used to work for me. He is a good man, but he has joined a Ukrainian guerrilla group. He came to warn me today that the group has been attacking farms and estates nearby and that we might be a target. Ola will be safer away from here.'

Ten minutes later, Ola left with Aniela and climbed into the truck she had brought. She was mystified as to why she had to leave so quickly, but realised there must be a good reason.

'We can take the truck quite near to the border, but will have to go by minor roads to avoid Soviet patrols. We will have to do quite a lot of walking, Ola,' Aniela told her, 'and you must be very quiet at all times. No talking at all once we are nearer Brest.'

Four hours later, Ola was walking through a forest towards the River Bug. She remembered all too clearly what had happened the last time she was near the border and hung back. Aniela took her hand and whispered, 'Don't be frightened, Ola. If we are careful to avoid the main crossing point, we should be able to cross over without meeting any soldiers. I have done this several times and I know where to cross the river. Because there is no moon tonight it will be easier.'

Ola held Aniela's hand tightly as they came nearer to the river. There was very little light and she tripped over tree roots at regular intervals. Suddenly she saw some men behind a tree and she stopped suddenly. 'Soldiers,' she whispered to Aniela.

To her surprise, Aniela went up to the men and said a few words. She came back for Ola. 'Don't worry Ola,' she said, 'Those men are in the underground army. They are on our side. They are going to blow up one of the bridges downstream from here and then leave in our truck. We must wait until we hear the bangs and then it should be safe to cross. Hopefully both Soviet and German patrols will be diverted.'

For an hour, Ola sat under a tree and waited with Aniela. She jumped when suddenly there was a series of muffled bangs followed by shouting, the sound carrying up the river and echoing off the trees. Aniela grabbed her hand and they made their way towards the bridge. Ola's heart was in her mouth as they moved across the bridge. Soon they were exposed, but there was no one shouting at them, no Soviet soldiers with guns. They set off into the darkness and she walked with Aniela for so long her feet started to hurt.

Twenty One

Halina, August 1940, Starodub Labour Camp

The second part of Halina's journey was quite short and she was hustled out of the train, by what she estimated was mid-morning, into a small town where broadleaved trees rose to a clear blue sky. The sun dazzled her as her eyes adapted to the sharp light. The colours around her seemed over-saturated, the greens too green, the blues too blue. After months starved of colour, having seen nothing but grey walls, she looked around her, eagerly seeking out the brightest colours and devouring the sight.

The small group passed many people in the streets. Most did not look in their direction, but turned away at the sight of the guard's uniform. At one corner however, an old woman stood, with her shawl wrapped round her head despite the warmth of the sunshine. She smiled at Halina as she passed close to her and whispered something that she did not fully recognise, but it seemed to indicate her sympathies and made her feel less alone.

All too soon, they stopped outside a large stone wall with a wooden gate. There was a large sign on the gate that indicated this was Starodub labour camp for the young. She felt fear returning. What would be waiting for her? Would there be more concrete, stone, metal bars, dirt and despair? Apprehensively she walked through the gate and then gaped in astonishment. At the end of a long drive was a large stone building with turrets and towers. There were domes and statues at each corner of the roof. The building sat at the centre of a large park. Green was everywhere - grass, trees and more grass. Bordering the drive and dotted throughout the parkland were large lime trees. The leaves were wonderful shades of soft green, and here and there, were already showing the orange tints of autumn and glowing in the golden light in the sun.

She had almost forgotten what grass looked like. Was she really coming here? Perhaps her cell would be in another building with barred windows blocked up to prevent her seeing the grass and trees. However, there was no barred cell. She was taken through a large wooden door into a hall with an ornate high ceiling. Was this really in Russia? A man in a uniform approached, and spoke slowly in Russian. She understood enough of what he was saying - she would be treated well if she worked hard. He led her up the staircase into a large room and pointed towards a bed. He made it clear that was her bed.

Halina felt the tension within her subsiding. She was not going to a cell. She was actually going to have a bed. She could hardly believe what she saw as she looked around. There were lines of beds on either side of the long room - about twenty beds in all. She moved towards a bed which had blankets and a sheet folded on the end, put her small bag on the bed and sat on it looking round. The walls were stone, and looked cold and austere, but the presence of beds and blankets softened the appearance. After a crowded, dirty, prison cell, it seemed like heaven.

The official started saying something and mimed washing. Halina opened her little bag and took out her tiny washcloth and her spare set of underwear, which was grey and rather worn from frequent washing, but reasonably clean. She followed him along the corridor and into another room with a steamy atmosphere. There was a basin with water, a small quantity of soap and a towel. In addition, there was a bottle of disinfectant for her hair and clothes. By dogged persistence and constant washing, she had managed to keep lice to a minimum in prison. Thank goodness she had been spared the necessity of a more thorough delousing.

The official told her again to wash, and left, closing the door behind him. The water was lukewarm, but there was enough steam in the room for her to feel warm. Moreover, there was a whole basin of water just for her. No more struggling with flakes of soap and cups of water. She could indulge in an orgy of washing. There was enough soap and water to lather all over several times.

By the time she had finished, her hair squeaked with cleanliness and her skin began to take on a withered look. Finally satisfied, she rinsed off the soap. There was a towel to dry with, not just a tiny washcloth. Not only could she put on clean underwear, she had more than enough water and soap to wash her dirty clothes properly. She squeezed out as much water as she could, and with her hair damp and smelling faintly of disinfectant, she ventured out into the corridor again. As she left the room, she wrapped the soap in her washcloth and took it with her. She might not be allowed such luxury again.

There was no one about, so she walked back to the dormitory and hung her damp clothes over the window ledge. There were several other items there and she had to squeeze them up to make room. She sat on the bed to wait for the official to return. If the sleeping and washing conditions were this good, perhaps life here would be bearable. Even without Mama.

The official came back and walked her along the corridor and down the stairs again. He explained his role in the labour camp and although Halina did not understand all his words, he was able to make her understand that she would have school each morning and that she would be with other Polish girls in a lower form as she spoke little Russian.

Halina stopped listening at that point. He had said 'the other Polish girls'. That meant she was not alone. They walked along another long corridor then stopped at a wooden door.

'Your school,' the official said and opened the door.

This time a woman who appeared the same age as her grandmother met her. She introduced herself as Maria and told her in slow and beautifully modulated tones that she was her teacher. Halina was greatly relieved that there was at least one woman in the building. What was more she seemed a sympathetic soul.

She sat down next to another girl who greeted her in Polish, saying her name was Stasia. The girl was about her own age with blonde hair cut quite short, and with a fringe that framed her pale blue eyes. Halina was thrilled to meet a fellow Pole and she looked closely at the girl. She appeared healthy and well fed without any bruises or wounds to suggest that life was anything other than ordinary. Would she get something other than soup and bread here?

'It is not too bad here if you work hard,' Stasia whispered. 'We have school in the morning - that is usually bearable, except when they start on about Stalin. Did you see that statue when you came in? At every opportunity, they go on about how wonderful Stalin is, how he loves his people and so on. We just have to grin and bear it, but it is difficult to keep quiet.'

Halina was about to reply when a bell sounded.

'Lunch,' came the whisper. 'There are several dining rooms. If we work hard enough we get good food and a better dining room. You will hear all about Stakhanoviet soon enough.'

They filed out and she followed Stasia to the dining room where she sat at a table with nine other girls, who she discovered to her joy were all Polish. The meal consisted of soup, but thick, and quite tasty, and served with white, crusty bread. She put some in her pocket for later, just in case. She might not get that amount of bread every day.

After lunch, there was half an hour or so free, and the girls took Halina outside and into the grounds. She stood, distracted by the green and gold again. They had so much freedom – it was hardly like a prison at all. She tried to take in what the girls were saying, but there was too much information. She was tired and emotional and thoughts of Mama kept buzzing round her head. She told how with her mother and sister, she had been arrested crossing the border, and briefly described her time in prison.

However, it was so hard to describe how Ola had been taken away, and harder still to tell of the recent separation from Mama. Why did her voice keep trembling? The other girls each told a little of how they had come to be there. Many had a similar story - they had been betrayed by guides or by bad luck and had been arrested crossing the border. They seemed almost too cheerful at times. Perhaps they too were holding back on the worst of the details for fear of showing too much emotion. Everyone had suffered as much as she had.

Twenty Two

Halina, August 1940, Starodub Labour Camp

It seemed that Starodub labour camp was a showpiece. Being a day or two's journey from Moscow, it was visited by various dignitaries from time to time who were shown just how well the girls were treated, and how much was done to turn them into model Soviet citizens. School was each morning and in the afternoon was work - weaving and sewing.

'I hope you are given sewing,' said Stasia, 'the weaving shed is awful. There is cotton dust everywhere and it makes some people ill. It is heavy work but occasionally we get some spoiled pieces and we would try to make clothes from them, but we do not have any tools.'

'The evenings are the worst,' said another girl. 'We have talks and films, singing and dancing. It is hard to bear.'

Halina was puzzled. Why should singing, dancing and films be hated? Surely that was something to be enjoyed? Another bell sounded and they made their way to the main building. She was unsure where to go until an official in a NKVD uniform approached and motioned her to follow him. She was led into a sewing factory with rows of what she discovered were interlock machines. At each machine a girl sat crouched over her work. Most of the girls in the labour camp were Russian it seemed. Rather like the prison in Homel.

Halina sat at the sewing machine. She had no idea what to do, but if she did not learn quickly, she might not be treated well. She did not want to return to prison conditions. She looked around at the Soviet girls, who appeared to be working industriously. Surely if they could do it, someone who was altogether more intelligent and educated must be able to. She must grit her teeth, concentrate hard and listen carefully to the instructions given. The fact they were in Russian did not help.

Eventually she understood what was required and her first garment was finished. It was rather misshapen and she had missed the seam in a few places, but it was a good first effort. By the third and fourth garment, she felt more competent. Her arms ached and her fingers were sore where she had somehow managed to prick them with the needle. Nevertheless, she had succeeded.

By the time the bell rang to signal the end of work, she was tired both physically and emotionally. She sat in the dining hall for the evening meal. The girls were talking to her, but she was so tired she could not take in what was being said. Besides, she was entranced by the food. It was real food. Not just soup and bread. There was some kind of fish, potatoes and even some vegetables. The quantities were very small and the quality poor, but every mouthful seemed heavenly compared to her previous diet. The girls were telling her about the evening activities, but she did not hear them. The food had to be savoured.

That evening, Halina was treated to the story of Stakhanov, a Russian miner who managed a prodigious output and from whom the Stakhanoviet movement was derived. She did not understand all that much due to her limited knowledge of Russian, but the girls filled her in on the detail when they were back in the dormitories. Their aim, it seemed, was to be a Stakhanoviet worker. For this, they had to achieve more than a certain rate of working called the norm. If they did less, they would be punished by receiving poorer food and conditions. If they achieved more than the norm they would receive better food, a better dining room and better conditions. They would also receive a few more roubles for their work.

Halina was worn out by the end of the day, but as she lay in bed that night, her attempts to make sense of the day's events kept her awake. It was confusing. When living under Soviet occupation, and when in prison, she had known how she should feel. The Soviets were the enemy and she obstructed them whenever possible. Knowing who to hate had helped her to cope with the worst of the conditions. She had been defiant. She was sure Poland would become free again some day and she had to be there to see it. However, here at Starodub it was very different. She had a decent bed to sleep on, food to eat, and work which would allow her to improve her conditions. It did not make sense. Why did a nation that tried to destroy everything Polish now treat her well? As she lay puzzling out her situation, she fell asleep, lulled by the familiar sound of Polish voices.

Halina decided to stand a little on the sidelines for the next few days. She would talk with her Polish group, work in her lessons and continue to improve at her sewing, but she would reserve her judgement until she had worked out what to feel about her situation. The answer came in the sewing hall when one of the Soviet girls turned to her.

'Gala, is it true your father is an officer in the Polish army?' she asked

'Yes,' Halina replied.

'Then you should kill him.'

Halina looked at her aghast. 'Are you stupid,' she squeaked. 'Why would I want to do that, he is my father.'

'He is an officer and an enemy of the Soviet people,' was the reply, 'you should kill him.'

Halina sat stunned by the words. What kind of country was this that said it was acceptable to kill your father? What had they done to these girls? Then she realised what was happening. It was obvious. The aim was to control their minds. Everything that had happened in Poland so far was designed to kill the Polish spirit, to destroy the Polish way of life. Anyone thought of as a danger, was arrested, killed or deported. However, she was here with the other girls so that they could be turned into model Soviet citizens. Controlling their work rate with promises of better conditions, lecturing them on Stalin, singing about the Soviet Revolution, much of the teaching in school, all was aimed at destroying their nationalism and replacing it with Soviet ideals. Well they underestimated the Polish spirit if they thought they would control her mind!

She had found her battleground, and at last was clear how to tackle life in Starodub. Let the NKVD think she was being controlled, but rebel in subtle ways. She would be subversive. The Resistance girls in Brest prison had told her how. She would talk to the other Polish girls and they would decide what to do.

'It seems to me that we should aim to be Stakhanoviet workers,' said Stasia. 'Not only would the improved conditions be worth working for, it would also show what good workers Polish girls could be, despite being away from home. That will show them how much better we are.'

It was after the evening lectures and the group of Polish girls was in the garden with Halina, discussing strategy. The main dissenter was a girl called Anita, whose earlier experiences had left her very bitter. 'I will not be manipulated by them,' she declared, 'You are just doing what they want.'

'Anita,' replied Halina, 'perhaps working hard will help our enemy and we should be as difficult as possible, but on the other hand would the Soviets really defeat our soldiers just because we sew a few more skirts? It seems to me that others will judge Polish people on what we do and how we behave. Perhaps when the Soviet girls see how capable we are, they might have doubts about their Stalinist ideals.'

'Perhaps you are right,' Anita sighed, 'but if we do well in school and work, what can we do to be subversive?'

'We will think of things when they arrive,' added Lucia, a quiet, dark-haired girl Halina had not heard say much until then, 'but first we must make them think we are doing what they want by working hard.'

Now she had the support of the other girls in the 'underground' battle with the Soviets, and was more in control of her situation, Halina expected to feel less unhappy, but thought of her mother continually. She worried a great deal about her. Would she cope without her daughters? She had been so distraught when the guards had taken Ola away. What if she lost her mind as she so nearly had before? What was it like in her labour camp? Was she getting enough food? Was it cold? As she brooded, she realised that what she found hardest to bear, was the fact that she had no way to influence her mother's state of mind as she had in prison.

Frustration and worry gnawed at her. That night, after the planning meeting in the gardens of the camp, she lay in bed holding Eugenia's silk shawl. There was the faintest touch of perfume left which comforted her, but it was only after she had cried herself to sleep, that finally she had some peace.

Ola, August 1940, Western Poland

When Ola awoke it was dawn, and fingers of light were poking through the door hinges of the wooden hut. She lay sleepily for a minute trying to recall the night before. She had walked a long way in the dark with Aniela, she remembered, until at last they had arrived at a wooden house where there was a friendly face and some food. She must have fallen asleep almost immediately afterwards, because she did not remember going to bed. Aniela spoke to her.

'After breakfast, Ola, we will get a wagon to a railway station about thirty miles from here, and then we can get the train to Warsaw.' Ola started to say that she was pleased that she did not have to walk again when Aniela continued, 'The trains stop about ten miles from Warsaw as most of the train lines have been blown up, so we will have to walk the rest of the way, I'm afraid. There is a curfew at 7pm, so if we arrive too late we will have to wait until morning.'

The trip to the station was uneventful, if uncomfortable, but once on the train, Ola could see that Aniela was nervous. She had said something to Ola about forged papers and hoping that there would not be too many checks on the train, but she was not worried. Soon she would be in Warsaw. Perhaps even Papa would go there some day.

The motion of the train made her feel sleepy again as she was still tired from the long walk of the night before, and she fell asleep, her head leaning on Aniela's shoulder.

Aniela looked around the carriage at the other passengers. There were three women with large bags and a very elegant man with a suitcase. The women looked like smugglers to her. Food was becoming more difficult to find and items such as meat and grain were usually obtained from the black market or by smuggling. As the women had boarded the train at a rural station, she guessed they were bringing food from some farm or other to sell in Warsaw. She hoped that if there were checks on the train, the women would divert attention from her and Ola.

Her papers were good forgeries, but they would not withstand scrutiny. When she travelled on her own, she had many tricks to avoid checks – hiding in the toilet and leaving the door wide open was one, but she would not be able to take avoiding action so easily with Ola. She had purposely taken the train from a station some miles from Brest, as there were more checks on the trains near the border. She hoped that the mere presence of Ola would protect her.

When they were about thirty miles from Warsaw, police boarded the train together with two men in long coats, who Aniela suspected were Gestapo. They seemed to be checking all papers very thoroughly and were moving slowly through the carriage. They stopped at the women with the bags and one of the policemen cut one of the bags open. A bag of grain spilled onto the carriage floor followed by several bottles of wine. The other bags were opened and similar contraband exposed.

The Gestapo took some time talking to the women while the policemen confiscated the goods, and by the time they reached Aniela, they only glanced at her papers. They carried on along the carriage, but not before Aniela noticed several bottles of wine had found their way into the pockets of the long coats. She sat back in her seat and sighed with relief.

Ola had slept through the excitement and only woke up when Aniela shook her gently to say they had arrived at their destination. 'We will have to sleep in the station, I'm afraid, Ola, as we would not get to Warsaw before the curfew, but we should be able to get a drink here at least.'

As the sun rose the next morning, Ola was once more walking, after having spent an uncomfortable night on the station floor. The roads were busy with people and cars, but most seemed to be leaving Warsaw, hoping for better conditions and less interference from the invaders in the country districts.

'In some ways it is safer in Warsaw,' Aniela told her, 'It is much easier to be insignificant in a large town.'

As they walked, Ola talked about Halina and her mother, and told Aniela about the way they had moved around to try to avoid the NKVD. Thinking about her mother still hurt, but talking about her made her seem more real. She knew everyone else worried that she had gone to Siberia, but she understood little of what that entailed. Knowing she would see Granny and Auntie Janina soon helped to cheer her up and to forget just how much her feet hurt.

Exhausted, thirsty and hungry, finally she arrived at Janina's door and was greeted with hugs, kisses and many tears. That night she was shown to yet another bed by her aunt and as she kissed her good night she asked, 'Do you think I will ever see Mama and Halina again?'

Janina held her tightly, 'We will never stop looking for them, my dear,' she replied,

'For now, you will be my daughter.'

That was not the answer Ola wanted, but it would have to do. She did not know that Titov had received some news from his Resistance colleagues. Not long after she had left with Aniela, Ukrainian guerrillas had attacked Jan's estate, as he had feared. Everyone had been killed. If Ola had not left, she would have been among the dead.

Twenty Three

Eugenia, September 1940, Siberia

The swaying of the train made it difficult to talk to anyone except those nearest to her, but when it stopped, it was possible to move about a little. However, the circumstances under which Eugenia first talked to Marysia were rather different. The train stopped in the middle of nowhere, the doors opened and everyone was told to get out. At first Eugenia thought they had arrived at their destination, but she was wrong. When the prisoners struggled out of the train, limbs stiff from inactivity and bruised from frequent contact with the swaying sides of the truck, they were told to spread out along the length of the train. Eugenia was terrified. Where they going to be executed? What other reason could there be for lining them up? The guards shouted at them.

'Remove your undergarments, squat and relieve yourself.'

Eugenia thought she had not heard correctly, but the command was repeated several times and the backs of those nearest the guards were prodded roughly. Fearing a bullet in the back, everyone complied. Once she realised she was not about to be executed, Eugenia felt so relieved she quickly did as bid. She would even have found some humour in the situation, had not shame at the degradation shone from the faces around her. However, these were mainly people who had only recently been arrested. Perhaps they had not yet suffered as she had. What was a little humiliation compared to having your children taken from you? She replaced her skirts with a flourish. They had not succeeded in degrading her.

She noticed a young woman next to her, struggling to cope with a baby and a young boy. The boy was about four years old with golden curls and an angelic face, now dirty from weeks of travelling. 'Don't let it upset you,' she said to the woman, whom she discovered was called Marysia, 'they are trying to degrade us, but they will not succeed if we do not let them.' Marysia smiled weakly,

'You are so brave. How do you do it?'

'I have had months to adjust,' said Eugenia, 'and at least we are still alive. That is what matters most. Then we can pray for help.'

Seated once again in the truck, Marysia told her story. 'My husband is an officer in the Polish army. I do not know what has happened to him. People say some soldiers escaped and the Germans or the Soviets captured others. I was alone in the house with my children when they came to the door at night. I had been planning to go and stay with my mother later in the week and had a large case packed, so I had time to collect food and pack it. I hope the cases are on the train somewhere.'

As Marysia talked, Eugenia noticed how quiet and pale the baby was. 'How have you coped in the heat with the baby?'

'I am still feeding her myself, but there does not seem to be much milk. I am not getting enough water myself to drink. Josef seems to be coping better now.' Her son looked up as he heard his name, and Eugenia pulled him towards her.

'Would you like to hear a story Josef?' The little boy looked at her gravely, put his finger in his mouth and nodded his head. Eugenia told him the stories she used to tell Halina and Ola when they were small, and found she benefited from the experience as much as the child did. Holding the small body on her knee was comforting, and helped reduce the terrible ache of longing for her own children. Wherever her children were, she hoped that someone was helping them.

As the train pressed deeper into Russian territory, the air became cooler. Once or twice, there was heavy rain and several of the men managed to loosen some wooden planks in the roof to allow water to enter. The planks were replaced hastily at each stop in case the guards noticed. The water was eagerly collected and passed around, although there was little more than enough to moisten the tongue. The activity gave the impression that they had gained a little control over their situation, and Eugenia saw a few faces become less drawn as a result. However, it did little to improve the terrible conditions in the truck, and the small amount of rainwater did little to clean the accumulating filth near the toilet hole.

To help take her mind off her own problems, Eugenia studied her fellow travellers throughout the journey. She could see that it was very difficult for the men. They were unused to ceding all control, and obviously many felt that they had somehow let their families down by not protecting them. It was heartbreaking to see such men in tears of shame and despair. She knew how they felt - she had failed to protect Ola and Halina.

Women with children seemed the stronger mentally as they thought mainly of their children's needs, as she had, but fear for their children's future showed in their every movement, every turn of the head, every action. It did not make sense though. Ola had been taken from her because she was too young to go to prison, yet there were whole families on the train, from tiny babies to ancient grandparents. Moreover, Marysia had been arrested, yet was able to keep her children. 'I think I was just lucky,' she had said when Eugenia asked her about it. She looked around the truck. Was it good luck to have your children with you in these surroundings?

There were several old men and women who gazed ahead, stoic and uncomplaining. Perhaps they felt they had led their life and had nothing to lose. There were children of Halina's age and younger, who complained loudly at the physical conditions and lack of food, but their spirit seemed less affected than their parents. One girl was very like Halina. She was irritated with the guards, angry at the lack of food, but she also showed great tenderness to an old woman who was obviously her grandmother.

Watching the girl talking animatedly to some young people in another carriage at one of the stops, gave Eugenia a strange feeling of relief. Perhaps Halina was adjusting to being away from her. Perhaps she had found friends to help her through the difficulties. Her heart lifted and for the first time since Halina had left, she felt a little optimism. When Kazimierz had been at home, she had wished that Halina had been less defiant. Now she realised it could be the saving of her.

When the train stopped for the last time, spirits rose a little. Surely nothing could be worse than the nightmare conditions in the train? Eugenia jumped down from the truck and helped Marysia with Josef. The baby was still very quiet and pale and Eugenia feared it might not survive. The station was packed with hundreds of bewildered, frightened faces. Eugenia just managed to contain her own anxiety, but as she looked at the faces of those around her, she could not help but be affected by their terror and anguish.

Several NKVD officials stood around shouting orders, and eventually Eugenia found herself in the back of a lorry taking them along a track that became rougher with each mile. After an hour of discomfort, they were told to get out and to walk the last few miles. Although it was early September, already the air was cold, and as they walked along the track, a few flakes of snow floated past. 'We left in summer and arrived in winter,' she said to Marysia who was walking beside her, trying to encourage Josef.

'He is so tired,' she said, 'I hope we do not have to walk far. I am not sure he will make it.'

Eugenia carried her small bag in one hand and Marysia's in her other, so that Marysia could carry the baby and hold Josef's hand. Several of the others with them were struggling with larger bags. One suitcase burst open and its contents spilled across the track. The owner, a young woman in her twenties, desperately tried to cram everything back in. One of the guards advanced with his rifle butt ready, but hands came from all sides to help and the case was packed and tied with a belt before he arrived. There were no men in her party, and very few children. Someone said that most of the families on the train had gone on to another camp and that only women on their own were with her group. She could not decide if that was good or bad.

The track was edged with tall pine trees, and in the distance, Eugenia could see glimpses of the blue and silver ribbon of a river twisting its way through the forest. Further still were mountains, already capped with snow. In other circumstances, it would have been a beautiful sight, but she had no energy left to appreciate beauty, and longed to be able to sit down, to wash and to eat.

Light was fading fast as they arrived at the camp, a collection of large wooden barracks and huts. The camp officials sent Eugenia and Marysia to a cabin situated at the end of one of the large barracks. The cabin was about twelve feet by fifteen and made from logs, with moss pushed between the logs for insulation. In one corner was a small stove, and there was a sink in another corner with a toilet bucket next to it. There were double bunks at each end and a small table in the middle. There were already several people in the cabin when they arrived, and another six arrived not long afterwards. By the time everyone was inside with bags, there was no room to move and Eugenia had to stand up with the rest, while introductions took place.

There was a woman about her age, Janka, transferred from one of the larger barracks with her three teenage daughters, and a woman in her sixties, who insisted they call her Mrs Reginella. In addition to Marysia, with her baby and Josef, there was Mr and Mrs Pieczko, a couple in their seventies, Sabina and Karolina, two sisters in their early twenties, and finally a young woman in her thirties called Teresa. Eugenia soon discovered that Teresa's young daughters had been taken from her before she boarded the train in Poland.

Janka spoke first, 'We are very lucky to have this place,' she said, 'I was in one of the larger barracks when I arrived in March, but it became so crowded with new people arriving each month, that they had to build some huts. It is very cramped here, but it will be much easier to keep clean with a small number of people, and provided we organise ourselves properly, we should find life a little less difficult.' She was a plump woman in her forties and Eugenia was surprised that she looked so healthy. 'I had a lot of extra fat to feed off,' she admitted later that evening to Eugenia, 'There is still some more and then I will be as thin as everyone else.'

Having someone around who knew how the camp worked, had a positive effect on morale, and soon the whole group was contributing to organisation. They decided to share all the food, and even those who had brought food in their luggage agreed to this. The bunks were allocated on an age basis with the younger girls and Josef sleeping on the floor.

'Lice,' said Janka, once everyone was settled, 'you must be ready for lice, and bedbugs.'

'Do you have to be so coarse about it,' complained Mrs Reginella, looking down her nose at Janka.

'Lice will feed off anyone,' Janka replied, ignoring the comment, 'but we will be able to boil underwear on the stove and must try to keep our hair clean. Not much we can do about the bedbugs I'm afraid, they live in the moss.'

Surprisingly, the discussions had a calming effect on Eugenia and she did not even mind Janka's rather bossy manner. The worst part of her arrival was fear of the unknown. Now they had some kind of structure, perhaps life would not be so bad. Exhausted by the day's events she fell asleep quickly and slept soundly, despite having to share a hard wooden bunk with Mrs Reginella.

Twenty Four

Eugenia, September 1940, Siberian Labour Camp

A gong woke them before seven the next morning. Janka collected their bread ration, but once the bread arrived they had no time to eat it, so Marysia divided it up and kept some for their return. She was given the job of looking after the small group of young children already in the camp, together with her own children. Much to Eugenia's relief, Marysia's baby seemed a little better, although that had the disadvantage that it had cried much of the night.

'It is good to be with a smaller group,' said Marysia, 'it would be impossible to have such harmony if we were in the big room with a hundred other people.'

'It is fine as long as we don't fall out.'

Eugenia raised her eyebrows. It was ironic that Mrs Reginella should say that. She was the one most likely to upset people with her imperious manner. However, she was older, and apparently had been very wealthy, so perhaps it was difficult for her to adjust. Janka had given everyone advice on how to dress for work, and found some rags for Eugenia to tie round her hands as she had no gloves. 'They help reduce the chafing and should stop the worst of the blisters.'

As they lined up for roll call with the rest of the camp, Eugenia estimated that there were about 300 people in the camp, all of them women, except for a few, who were either old or very young.

'The men were moved to another camp,' said the woman next to her when Eugenia asked why there were no men. 'At least that is what they told us,' she added.

The Commandant started telling the new arrivals that they would be divided into brigades and would go into the forest to cut trees. Eugenia was not sure how she would manage that, but before she had time to think, they were being marched out of the gate in groups. She was in a group of fifteen, led by the brigadier, who was Russian and a former prisoner. They walked for several miles along a muddy track, across which trees had fallen in places. It was cold and the sun was just starting to rise.

'What will it be like when winter starts in earnest,' Eugenia turned to Janka.

'Dark and well below freezing. It was minus twenty degrees here when we arrived in March.'

'Are we really expected to cut down trees?'

'Yes,' replied Janka, 'and make sure those rags round your hands are tied properly, you will get terrible blisters otherwise.'

Before long, they arrived at a small clearing where felled trees were stacked in one place, and cut logs and sticks in another. The brigade leader handed out saws and pointed out the trees they were to cut down, and then left to visit another group. Janka picked up a long saw and told Eugenia to take the other end. She looked carefully at the trees before finally choosing one.

'It is best to get those with as narrow a trunk as possible,' she explained to Eugenia, 'Also the tree should have a clear area to fall into.'

Having selected the tree, they started sawing. Eugenia looked around. The trunk seemed very thick, but others nearby were even thicker at the base. The thought of sawing through them was daunting. She pushed and pulled at her end of the saw, but it hardly moved. After an hour, the blade had only moved in a few inches and she was already exhausted. The teeth snagged in the bark and the sawing became even more difficult with time. She longed for a rest. Surely they would have to stop to eat sometime? Her shoulders ached from the constant motion, her head pounded from the effort of pushing and pulling.

She looked at her hands, which had become painful. Large blisters had formed despite the rags wound round her hands. Sawing horizontally was awkward, and she could not prevent the saw wandering off a straight line. Janka said for the fourth, or was it the fifth time, that they must keep the saw horizontal, otherwise they would make an angled cut which would take longer. She was trying to keep the blade horizontal but it was so difficult. Would they stop for a rest? No. She had to keep sawing. The blisters throbbed and ached. Her hands felt as if they were on fire. But she had to keep sawing.

Eventually they stopped briefly to eat the bread they had brought and to drink hot water. Someone had been allocated the task of lighting the fire, which was used to boil water for drinking as well as to burn the brushwood from the trees. The sweet smell of pine scented the air, but the break gave only a momentary relief from the grinding toil. Once she had eaten the bread, she had to start sawing again.

By the end of the day, they had managed to saw through just three small trees. Eugenia walked wearily back to the camp, carrying small logs for the stove, Perhaps the work would become easier with time. She had to keep positive. She must believe it would become easier.

That evening she talked to Mr and Mrs Pieczko, who had said very little to anyone since they had arrived. Mr Pieczko had owned a small woodworking business and had been set to work using his skills around the camp. His wife had worked in the forest when she first arrived, but was now too weak to work.

'We have lost everything.' Mr Pieczko spoke quietly, his arms round his wife who was in tears. 'Our son was arrested and we do not know where he went, and then they came in the middle of the night and told us to leave.' His wife started sobbing louder at that point. 'We are too old to work. We have nothing to live for anymore. My wife is so unhappy in this terrible place and we have been here since March.'

Eugenia could not think of anything to say to them. It was obvious that Mrs Pieczko was fading and would not last many more weeks. She thought of the old woman on the train, and feared that the camp officials would regard Mrs Pieczko with the same lack of compassion.

When Eugenia woke the next day, her back was stiff and her arms ached from the unaccustomed hard physical work. She dreaded another day, but hoped the work would ease her stiff muscles. The temperature had fallen sharply in the night, and the onset of winter had become more than a hint. The track that had been muddy the day before was hard on the surface, and the small puddles peppering its length were frozen. Snow started to fall gently as they walked, the large white flakes floating down in slow motion. The group leader told them they were expecting a delivery of felt boots and other winter clothing, but made it clear they would have to buy them.

Their task was to cut up the trees it had taken them all day to fell, and then to chop the sections into sticks using axes. This time the sawing was a little less difficult as they did not have to struggle to keep the saw horizontal – keeping the blade vertical was easier. Chopping the wood into sticks used another set of muscles, the process made more difficult by the fact that the axes were not very sharp. However, they were sharp enough to cut human flesh, and Vala, Janka's eighteen-year-old daughter, received a deep gash on her leg when the blade slipped. Janka tore off part of her skirt to bind the wound, and Vala sat near the fire shivering with cold and shock until the day's work was over.

Without proper medical care, Vala's wound festered, and a week later, she died from blood poisoning. Her body was wrapped in cloth, and buried in a clearing in the woods, near the camp. Janka's normally ebullient nature was severely affected by Vala's death, and the funeral was a sad, dispiriting affair with the whole group mourning the loss of the bright, cheerful girl who had rarely complained, despite the pain of her wound. Eugenia could not help but reflect that the girl was not much older than Halina. What if she also became ill? Would she receive the same lack of care? However, there was no point in worrying so much when she could do nothing. She would make herself ill and that would help no one. Repeatedly, she told herself she must learn to cope so she would be there for her children when the war ended.

A few days after Vala's death, Mrs Pieczko died and soon after, her husband joined her. The camp doctor pronounced their deaths as due to pneumonia, but Eugenia suspected Mr Pieczko had died of a broken heart. He felt he had nothing to live for and had given up the fight.

As the days progressed, the unpleasant conditions become impossible to ignore. With hard work, they managed to keep lice to a minimum, but bed bugs multiplied quickly with many extra bodies to feed on. It was cold and the small stove did not throw out much heat. Coming home each day cold and exhausted, there was little will to keep clean, to wash clothes, to fetch water and to keep the stove fed with fuel. Worst of all was the lack of food. Even with the extra food brought in luggage, there was not enough to replenish the energy used by the backbreaking work. Eugenia worried that, with winter approaching, illness and malnutrition would weaken them further. Keeping up morale was vital. The death of the Mr and Mrs Pieczko was a warning of what happened once hope had gone.

One evening, several weeks after Vala's death, Eugenia discussed the morale of their group with Teresa. 'I think we need to do more to try and keep everyone positive,' she said. 'As it is we come home from work, eat, wash and worry until we fall asleep.'

Teresa nodded, 'All too often we talk about how difficult the work is, or about the people who have died that week.' Teresa was blonde and pretty, but the loss of her children and the weeks of insufficient food had left her face looking pale and bony. 'I know how upset I was that my children were taken from me in prison, but I would not wish them to suffer this place, so perhaps it was for the best.'

'We need some entertainment,' Eugenia continued, 'I can recite poetry and I know Marysia can sing.'

To their surprise, Mrs Reginella interrupted, 'I used to write plays for my children when they were little, so I could manage something for us. And do call me Monika. I was a little standoffish at the beginning, I know. But after sharing lice and body odours for several weeks, I think I could share my name with you.'

To everyone's amusement, Mrs Reginella had the job of cleaning the quarters of the Commandant and some of the NKVD officers in the camp. For someone who had never cleaned anything in her life, it must have been a humiliating experience, but she did not complain as she was spared the torture of hard physical work in freezing weather, and she knew how lucky she was to have a relatively easy job. 'I can procure some paper and pens from the Commandant's office,' she added. 'He will not notice if I am careful.'

An impromptu concert took place immediately and to everyone's surprise, Mrs Reginella was the star of the show. She was not much younger than Mr and Mrs Pieczko, and had come from a wealthy background, but she had an indomitable spirit. She took some of Eugenia's poems and recited them in true comic fashion. The concert finished with the younger members of the group singing Polish folk songs, followed by everyone singing hymns. Mrs Reginella had reminded them that religious meetings were forbidden, so the singing was very quiet. By the end, even Janka joined in. 'We should do this at least once a week,' she said to Eugenia, 'I even managed to forget Vala for a time. I agree with Teresa, Giena, be thankful your daughters are not here to suffer.'

The concert raised Eugenia's spirits, and the comments of Janka and Teresa comforted her. It was better that Halina and Ola were spared the cold and the overwork she endured. She must convince herself that she was happy they were not with her. She felt herself drifting off to sleep. Thank God she was part of such a group of friends who could support each another. She had seen too many who had given up hope or who had to struggle on alone. Life in the camp was becoming more unpleasant by the day, but she would be able to survive much longer with others to help her.

Winter soon arrived in earnest. There were several feet of snow on the ground, and temperatures of fifteen below zero, with the promise of worse to come. By some miracle, Eugenia had obtained a jacket, some winter boots and gloves, using part of the precious store of roubles sewn into her ermine collar. Any thoughts of keeping the money for longer were dashed, as the alternative was freezing to death.

She was thankful for the extra protection from the cold the next day, as she trudged along the familiar track in the forest. The snow was frozen hard on the surface and crunched under her feet. Every now and then, where rocks or the tree canopy had prevented the snow from freezing hard throughout, the surface gave way, dragging a leg downwards, or worse, plunging her up to her waist.

As Eugenia dragged herself free, she castigated herself. She must be more careful. Extra energy was required to escape the snowdrifts, energy that she did not have to spare. However, she had several more energy-sapping falls, despite walking in the footsteps of those in front who had travelled safely.

As she walked, she thought of Halina and Ola and, in particular, ways that she might contact them. The camp inmates had recently been allowed to write letters to the outside world, but she had been told that no letters would be sent out of eastern Poland and certainly nothing could be sent to other labour camps. She would not be able to contact Kazimierz' mother and cousin, but why could she not contact Ola or Halina? Would the letters she had written to her sisters, Barbara and Stasia, and to her family near Brest, cause them trouble? They would link them to an officer's wife. Would they even arrive?

Rather than think about her problems, she thought back to the concert of the night before. The group had come back frozen and starving, but immediately filled the stove with wood they had carried back with them. Marysia had already collected snow to melt, as the pump was now frozen, Janka had collected together the evening soup and bread for the group, and finally they had added small quantities of the extra food they had brought with them.

Mrs Reginella had tidied up the hut and even put the lice-infested clothes to boil on the stove. Eugenia shook her head. She could scarcely believe the change in Monika. Her superior air had been replaced by a fierce determination to overcome all obstacles, whether hers or those of others. Monika would not listen when she said that she was too tired to recite, and said the concert had to take place. Left to her own devices she would have slept instead. Well. It could hardly be called a concert. Everyone was too exhausted for that. In fact, without the energies of Marysia and Mrs Reginella, it would probably not have taken place at all.

She had just recited a short poem and Marysia had sung one song, but prayers and hymns followed, quietly as usual, and there had been a lifting of morale afterwards. It had been worth the effort. Thank goodness two of their number had indoor jobs. They had the energy to rouse everyone into action.

Eugenia pulled her scarf tighter round her face. In fact, the concerts, short as they were, had become a vital part of their survival technique. She could not say it enough - thank goodness for friends. Everyone knew that the extra food was diminishing and when gone, a slow death from starvation would be the result, but no one mentioned it, and that way it could be ignored. The wind blew snow into her face. Something that could not ignored was the cold.

When they arrived at their destination in the forest, several of her group set about lighting a fire, while she collected snow for melting in a bucket. The brigade leader handed out shovels with the usual saws and axes and told them they had to dig out the roots of the trees they had been cutting down over the previous weeks. He then added an enormous iron pole to the collection of tools.

Eugenia looked at the first tree stump with a sinking feeling. The task he had given them was so difficult, how could they take a tree out by its roots? They were too weak. First, they had to dig out the frozen snow from around the tree roots and cut through the surface roots. Sawing the tree roots was hard work, but attempting to dig the frozen ground was even harder.

Eventually after the combined efforts of the whole group, one of the stumps was ready for removal. Eugenia tried to lift the iron pole but could not. The pole was very heavy and could only be lifted when four pairs of hand grasped the end. Then they had to push the point under the tree. Everyone pushed, strained, and finally succeeded, leaving the pole sticking upwards at an angle. Eugenia jumped up to reach the end of the pole and she hung there, arms straining. More of the group attached themselves.

The pole was so cold. What if her hands froze to it? She had seen that happen earlier to a woman from another group and the skin had been ripped off leaving her hands raw. She tried not to think about it and hung until the pole moved downward, slightly loosening the stump. It was such a relief to be able to let go of the pole. Now all she had to do was to wait for the blood to return to her fingers.

She took off her gloves and looked anxiously at her fingertips. If the blood did not start flowing soon, it would mean frostbite. She rubbed and blew them for several minutes, until the pain from returning blood caused her to cry out. She had to be thankful of the pain. It meant her fingers were still alive. The pole was moved to another position and the painful, straining process repeated. Lifting the pole each time and hanging from the end was exhausting, and when finally the day was over, only two roots had been freed. Eugenia struggled back to the camp, disheartened and at the point of collapse. She hardly had the strength to raise her soup bowl to her mouth.

After several weeks of exhausting work, freezing cold and insufficient food, Eugenia awoke one morning with a raging headache and a fever. She struggled to the camp doctor who took her temperature and gave her a pass saying that as her temperature was high enough, she could be excused work without losing all her work credits. Over the next week, her temperature rose higher and she developed a racking cough. Marysia looked after her, as well as the children, and brought her soup and hot water to drink, as well as helping her to the toilet bucket. Using the outside latrines would have been dangerous due to the extreme cold. Each day she took a little of the food store brought by those who had the time and foresight to pack it, and gave it to Eugenia.

'I cannot work in the forest again,' Eugenia said tearfully one day to Marysia, 'It will kill me.'

'You are strong Giena. You will be fine.'

But she knew Marysia was lying.

Twenty Five

Halina, September 1940, Starodub Labour Camp

As the days turned into weeks, the ache of loneliness became more bearable, and when she managed to stop worrying about her mother, Halina became less unhappy. A great part of this was due to Maria. She was fortunate in having her as a teacher. Maria had been well educated in pre-revolutionary times and was much more like the teachers she had in Poland. Halina noticed that she was careful always to present a good Soviet face to the world, and was even more careful what she said to the class, but it was obvious from her beautiful grammar and her delight in presenting the group with good Russian poetry and writing, that her heart had a strong 'white' Russian centre. Her kindness was in contrast to the education officers who were all men. They were not actually unkind to her as long as she showed that she was willing to work hard, but they were much more ready to dispense propaganda at every turn.

Maria also taught Russian language, which Halina found she learned more quickly than she expected. Many of the Russian words were similar to Polish, which made things easier. She was determined to learn as quickly as possible. After all, Mama could speak Russian, so it must be possible. Maria was delighted at her enthusiasm and pressed books on her to read. Halina looked forward to Maria's teachings and avidly read whatever she was presented with. It was such a relief that much of it was of high literary quality and relatively free of Soviet propaganda. Most of the other Polish girls in the group had the same attitude and Maria quickly became as fond of the Polish girls as they were of her.

'Such intelligent, good girls,' she exclaimed in delight, many times each lesson, her positive attitude being assisted by the fact that the remainder of the class was, largely, anything but able or hardworking.

There were several hundred girls in the labour camp between the ages of twelve and eighteen, although Halina only knew those in her dormitory or in her classes. The Soviet girls were a mixture. Many of them were defined as criminals, and their crimes ranged from stealing bread to murder. There were those who had refused to work and those who earned their living by prostitution. This group was distinguished by their crude language and behaviour, especially when talking to the education officers.

Another large group had come over the border to Russia from places such as Latvia and Hungary, or neighbouring parts of the Soviet Union. They appeared to have come because of communist fervour, having been willing victims of propaganda, and some still spoke avidly of their enthusiasm. However, Halina suspected many had left their homelands because of the extreme poverty they endured at home. The Soviet authorities had apparently been of this opinion, and instead of welcoming the willing conscripts, they arrested them and accused them of coming to Russia to take advantage of the superior Russian conditions rather than staying and developing Soviet ideals in their own country. Thus, young girls of thirteen and fourteen were put in a labour camp for three to five years, simply for crossing the border into Russia.

'It's crazy,' Anita said scornfully one evening, 'they arrest those girls for coming into Russia and us for trying to leave. It seems to me they arrest anyone who does not do exactly what they are told.'

Halina felt rather sorry for the girls from the neighbouring Soviet territories, especially one called Esta. She was from a small village in Asiatic Russia and at sixteen, was small and slim, with dark hair and large brown eyes. She was very pretty when she laughed, but much of the time, she had a haunted look in her eyes. It reminded Halina of some of the faces she had seen in prison - the face of despair, Mama had called it. Esta was quiet most of the time and avoided conflict when she could by steering clear of the more raucous elements.

One day Halina had found Esta in a quiet corner of the gardens, where she was sitting staring into space with an occasional tear rolling down her cheek. As she sat beside her and asked what was wrong, Esta eventually told her what had made her cry.

'I have been here three years,' she said, 'and today they told me I would be free in two weeks time.'

'Surely that is good news,' Halina said, puzzled. The thought of freedom would have filled her with joy.

'But they will send me back. Back to my home. My family is very poor. There are five of us, three sisters and a brother. When I left, mother was expecting another. There was never enough food for us. I lost two brothers who died when they were very small because there was not enough food. If I go back, it will make things worse. Here I have food. It is good here.'

'Perhaps they will not send you back and you could go to Moscow.'

'That would be worse. What would I do, where would I go? I know no one there, I would have nowhere to live.'

At that, she started crying again. Halina did not know what else to say. Did people really live in such poverty? It was hard to imagine. Why were there so many children if her parents could not feed them?

Two weeks later, Esta left, as she had predicted. Halina saw her as she walked out through the gate with a guard at her side. At the last minute, she turned and looked back with longing and despair. Halina felt an ache in her throat. The girl looked so unhappy. Her home life must truly be dreadful if she would rather stay in captivity. For a while, she thought of her, but it was not long before she pushed her to the back of her mind. She had to concentrate on her own survival.

As schoolwork became easier and the sewing work became more familiar, the Polish girls approached their target rapidly, until finally they worked at a rate 'over the norm' and became Stakhanoviet workers. At first Halina thought the talk of better treatment and food was more of the endless propaganda, but it did in fact materialise.

Food was allocated on a strangely named 'kettle' system. There were three 'kettles'. Kettle one was for those below the 'norm', kettle two for those who achieved the 'norm' and kettle three for those above the 'norm' rate of work. Each level had a strict ration of bread and quality of meals associated with it. They had now achieved kettle three, and were given three good meals a day, a separate dining area and a few more roubles, which allowed them to buy small items from the camp shop.

Even Anita, having swallowed her pride, and followed the will of the majority, seemed just as delighted as they were that they had reached the target, although she tried to hide it.

'Perhaps Anita is right,' Halina admitted to Stasia after the celebrations, 'perhaps we are being manipulated, but we still had a choice and we took the most logical path.'

Some time later, she found Anita on her own in the garden. 'What happened to you, Anita,' she asked, 'before you came here, I mean. I get the impression that you have seen something terrible.'

Anita looked at her for some minutes. 'It is difficult to talk about,' she said. She paused for another minute and Halina waited in silence, hoping that would encourage her to talk. It worked.

'I was in a prison before here,' she said, 'I was in a cell with thirty other women. It was hot, dirty and cramped. We had very little food and the soup often had insects floating in it. It was disgusting.' Halina recalled the animal eyes in the dreadful soup in Homel prison and blanched. Anita stopped for another few minutes and Halina sat quietly, waiting.

'One day,' she continued in a rush, 'One day the cell door opened and this woman was thrown in through the door. They had beaten her. Her face and body was covered with large, red, bleeding cuts. Her face was purple where they had hit her. But her head.... they had pulled out all her hair. Pulled it out by hand, bit by bit. Some bits of skin had been ripped off as well. They had accused her of belonging to some anti-revolutionary group or other. But she had done nothing. She was only eighteen for goodness sake. Once she had recovered a little, she told us about the torture that she and some others with her had received. It was so awful......I cannot bear even to think about it. Why are they doing this to us?'

Anita started shaking and Halina began to understand the reason for her rebellious behaviour and the bitterness that surrounded her like a halo.

'Anita,' she said putting her arm round the other girl's shoulders, 'somehow you must put it to the back of your mind and look for positive things. It is hard I know, but you must not let them win.'

'You are right, Halina, but it is so hard, so very hard.' Anita turned and wept into Halina's shoulder.

Despite her brave words, Halina found the encounter upsetting. All that talk of prisons reminded her of Mama and Ola. What if they were being badly treated? She left Anita and went up to the dormitory. There was no one around.

She sat on the floor and from her case took the small bottle of cologne she had bought earlier from the camp shop. She had seen some of the Soviet girls drinking cologne a few days ago and examined the bottle carefully. What on earth was it in cologne that made them drink it? There was nothing obvious on the label. The bottle was a tiny glass phial closed with a small stopper. She reached over, pulled the silk shawl from under her pillow, and rested it on her knees under the bottle. She tried to wedge her nail under the stopper lid in order to prise it off, but the bottle spun from her grasp and rolled under the bed. She felt around for it in panic. It would be a disaster if it were broken. She would not be able to afford another bottle for a week.

Finally she discovered it, dusty but unbroken in a corner near a bed leg. Thank God. Gripping it more firmly she pulled the stopper with her teeth and succeeded in removing it. The lid left a bitter taste on her tongue. How could those Soviet girls drink that? She spat the stopper into her hand. She leaned back against the bed and lifted the shawl to her nose. There was only a faint sour smell. She would have to use most of the cologne to make it smell of Mama.

She released a drop from the bottle and watched it spread over the silk. The vacuum in the bottle prevented any more drops from falling, so she turned the bottle upright again to let some air enter. It was a slow process. Thank goodness she had gone to a good school and studied a little about scientific matters. There. That was the last drop. She lifted the shawl to her face and closed her eyes. The cologne was not quite the same as Mama's had been, but it was close. She inhaled the scent.

Would she ever see Mama and Ola again? Tears ran down her cheeks and onto the shawl, mingling in small damp patches with the cologne. Would she ever leave this place and go home? She longed for some comfort, but there was no one to give it. However, for once there was no need to hold back her tears, as she was alone. She bowed her head on her knees and wept until the shawl was damp throughout.

Twenty Six

Halina, September 1940, Starodub Labour Camp

When lectures were not on the agenda, the evening activities in Starodub involved joining a club, which could be dancing, singing or drama. Part of the purpose of each club was to perfect various routines which could be performed for visiting dignitaries, the aim being to demonstrate the quality of the reforming teachings in the labour camp. For this, it was compulsory to wear a uniform of green tunics and red headscarves. Stasia had told Halina that none of the Polish group had wanted to join a club, and only joined when threatened with punishment. In the end, they had decided to join the choir - forced to join something, it seemed the lesser of evils. Certainly none of the group wanted to join the drama club as that might mean acting out scenes depicting the Soviet Union and Poland. The Soviets appeared to hold more than a few grudges against the Poles who had defeated them in 1920.

On Halina's first night, it had seemed that there would be a great deal to enjoy in the club. There was a man who played the guitar with great skill. His repertoire included revolutionary tunes, but he also played some old Russian melodies, which were often haunting and emotional. There was a group of gypsy girls in the camp, and they sang gypsy songs while dressed in gypsy costumes. Their songs were quite beautiful and contrasted well with the livelier tunes to which they also danced.

However, before long, Halina began to realise why the other Polish girls had resisted joining the club. Most evenings they had to sit in the auditorium while the education officers took to the stage and told them how wonderful, beautiful and kind Stalin was. She looked round at the Soviet girls who appeared to be listening avidly and taking in every word. It was not surprising how easy it was to influence them. After all, they had not experienced the cruelty and tyranny of the Soviet troops that she had in Poland, and they were never told anything but fairy tales. The meeting finished with a song praising Stalin and at the end of it, they had to sing 'Hurrah Stalin, Hurrah'. How could she sing that, knowing what she did? What of those who had been deported or arrested in Luck? Or those who had been killed for nothing other than owning land. What had they done wrong? Finally, there was that poor woman Anita had seen while in prison, the one who had been tortured. How could she sing Hurrah?

After the first choir meeting, the Polish girls stood outside and debated how to deal with the problem. It was dark and they were huddled in a doorway trying to keep out of the cold. They were careful to talk quietly as they did not want to be heard by the many potential spies. Then Stasia had a brainwave.

'I have just realised,' she said, pausing until she had the group's undivided attention, 'I have just realised that a Polish word for 'stupid' sounds very like 'hurrah', so instead of singing 'Hurrah Stalin, Hurrah' we can sing 'Durak Stalin, Durak.'

They did not have to wait long to put the plan into action, as the next evening they had to sing yet another song praising Stalin. The group sang loudly and with enthusiasm, much to the surprise of the education officers, who were more used to reluctance. The moment came when they had to sing 'Hurrah Stalin, Hurrah' and they continued smiling and added the Polish word instead. No one noticed. Afterwards the girls dispersed to their respective dormitories in high spirits. As Halina lay in bed, she remembered the incident and for the first time for months, she laughed aloud.

The group began to look forward to choir nights, waiting for the opportunity to repeat the minor rebellion. The education officers were very pleased with their apparent enthusiasm and they continued undiscovered for some weeks.

Halina's usual place in the choir was at the end of the row, and one evening an education officer was standing quite close to her as she sang. After looking at her he said,

'What was that you were singing, Halina?'

'Just Hurrah for Stalin,' she replied. She must try to look serious.

The minor rebellion did not last much longer, as once suspicions had been raised, the officials listened more closely and eventually realised the Polish girls were not singing what they should. They were taken to one side and told gravely that they must not be disrespectful to Stalin, or they would be sent back to prison or have their sentence increased. As punishment, they had to spend several nights in cells where they had only meagre rations.

Halina sat in her dark cell, eating bread that was almost black, and drinking thin tasteless soup, a diet similar to that she had in prison. The cell was not unlike the cell she had shared with her mother, but there was a big difference. In the Russian prisons, she had no control over her destiny, and had to endure all that came her way. Here, she had chosen to disobey. She smiled triumphantly. The victory was sweet. They had made fun of the system and Stalin in particular, and if the price paid was poor rations and surroundings for a few days, it was worth it. In prison she had been sad, lonely, frightened. Here she was in control, and in the cell as a direct result of her own deliberate actions. She had taken the first step on the road to subversion. Now she must take every opportunity to demoralise the Soviet girls when she could.

One day in early September some farmers from a local communal farm, or kolkhoz, came to the camp to deliver food and other items. Winter had started early and it was very cold. The girls were outside during one of their breaks when the farmers arrived. Halina was amazed at the poverty of their dress – their clothes seemed inadequate and their feet were wrapped in rags. She jumped up on a bench and started to mock them. 'Look at your farmers,' she said, 'They are dressed in rags. They have rags on their feet. In Poland even the poorest farmers have boots.'

She continued like this for a while, until an education officer arrived on the scene. He took her to the camp director who warned her that such talk was anti-revolutionary and that she would have her sentence increased if she continued. Halina looked suitably contrite but felt very superior underneath. As she sat in the auditorium during the evening lecture, she plotted. She would have to be careful, and use more subtlety in future. She would talk to the Soviet girls about Poland and how wonderful her life had been, and would try to explain how fair, and just Poland was. She would not condemn the Soviet regime directly -that would be dangerous – instead she would choose topics that she knew would compare unfavourably with the Soviet lifestyle. She grinned. Subversion stage two was underway.

Comparing the quality of clothes was an easy way to undermine the Soviet girl's morale. The few Polish clothes the group wore were of vastly superior style and material to those owned by the Soviet girls, and especially by the refugees. Stasia had some red silky pants that she always washed and looked after carefully. Halina suggested she washed them when the Soviet girls were around as she had seen them eying then enviously. The plan worked and one girl was heard to remark with disgust, 'Look at that! She wears better things on her bum than we do on our head.'

Halina's Polish school uniform was similarly noticed, especially her navy woollen tunic, which had been so studied by the Soviet girls in the train transporting her to Starodub. They had never seen fine woollen cloth. She only took it out occasionally to shake out the creases and refold it, but when she did, she used the opportunity to talk enthusiastically about the beautiful clothes that could be bought in Poland.

'My mother has beautiful ball gowns,' she would say, 'her favourite is a dark blue silk with a skirt that swishes when she walks.' At which point she would twirl an imaginary skirt and pretend she was dancing at a ball. She did not say that her mother had sold them all to pay her traitorous guide.

Twenty Seven

Eugenia, November 1940, Siberian Labour Camp

'Comrade Commandant, your death rate is too high. It will only get worse as winter progresses.' The NKVD inspector turned to Commandant Sulimov who was standing nearby, trying not to look as uncomfortable as he felt. 'They should last at least a year, possibly two. If they all die in the first few months, you will not come anywhere close to your work quotas. You will have to issue more winter clothing and increase the food rations. You have the equipment for a sewing section, so use it. And make sure your death rate comes down a little.' Lecture over, he opened the door and left.

That evening, the Commandant sat at his desk and poured himself a large vodka. It was not the first time an inspection had been critical, but this time he would have to do something. Such a pity, as he made a nice profit from selling the winter clothing. Still it would only be for a year or so, next winter he could go back to normal. He put his feet on the desk and leaned back.

He had several names ready for the sewing group, but he needed one more. Now who could he use in the sewing section? One of the newer woman, perhaps one who was ill, that way he could kill two birds with one stone, or not kill as the case may be. He sniggered at his joke and took another large swig. How about that Korbinska woman? She was likely to die if she did not have an easier inside job and she looked as if she would know how to use a sewing machine. Not only that, she could speak Russian, which would be very useful. After all, she would have to talk to the guards if she wanted their clothes to fit.

He smiled. Well that was that problem solved. Now he could concentrate on important things. And he poured another drink.

Eugenia wrapped the blanket round her shoulders and walked slowly to the Commandant's office. She still felt very weak and was not sure that the fever had really gone. It was so cold outside. She knocked at the office door and walked in trying to stand up straight, but not quite managing it.

'Aah Korbinska, come in.' Eugenia walked towards the desk and swayed on her feet, but she was not invited to sit. 'I understand you have been pronounced fit for work?'

Eugenia nodded, as she did not trust herself to speak. She knew she was ill – fit for work hardly described how she felt. If she had felt like this at home, she would have stayed in bed for weeks.

'As a concession, I have decided to allow you to work in the sewing room. You will sew uniforms for the guards and winter clothing for the camp. You will start tomorrow at seven. Now go.'

The news was so unexpectedly good Eugenia could not quite believe it. Would she really be spared those terrible days in the freezing forest? She felt energy rushing through her. It was just so wonderful. Now she had a chance. Now she might survive the winter. When the war was over, she would be able to look for Helena and Ola. If she worked hard enough, she might even be able to earn more food. That would help make up for the weeks when her friends had given her food she had not earned. They had been so good to her, now she could pay them back a little. She put her hand over her mouth as she coughed. Now she knew she would get better and that wretched cough would finally go. Feeling enervated she put some lice-infested clothing to boil on the stove. Now she could work harder at keeping clean.

Halina, December 1940, Starodub Labour Camp

Halina's first Christmas in captivity was upon her before she knew it. Her Polish friends had been working for some weeks to produce Christmas presents for each other. They had saved some of their meagre wages so that they could afford some of the small items in the camp shop, with talcum powder and cologne being favourites.

The problem of lack of money was solved by some ingenuity. Occasionally some of those who worked in the weaving shed were able to obtain small pieces of spoiled material, but could not decide how best to make use of them until they found some suitable pieces of wood and by carving the end, managed to make crochet hooks. After some experimenting, and a great deal of unravelling, Halina crocheted some scarves for her friends and even made herself some underwear. Although she did not have much to fill the bra, and the pants were rather scratchy, at least she would be warm that winter.

Halina was determined to have some kind of celebration for Christmas, and chose Christmas Eve, the traditional time for Polish celebrations. She thought of her last Christmas in Luck with her mother and sister and felt depression creeping up on her. She needed some activity to distract her.

On Christmas Eve, the group sat round their Stakhanoviet dining table and debated how they could celebrate Christmas without being censored by their Soviet captors.

'We should break bread and share it,' said Lucia, 'but we do not have wafer bread here.'

'Normal bread will have to do,' Halina said. She took her piece of bread, broke it into pieces and passed pieces to her friends. Everyone else stood up and followed her lead, so that all ten were passing pieces of bread to each other, as was the Polish custom.

The education officers and other officials in the dining room looked at them in puzzlement. 'What on earth are they doing?' could be heard from all corners of the hall. No one was sure what was going on, but as there seemed to be no disrespect to Stalin or anti-revolutionary message, nothing was said to the group. Towards the end of the meal, Anita stood up and started singing a Polish Christmas carol. The others eagerly joined her and the whole of the dining hall sat in silence as the Polish group sang their way through several songs. Halina poured all her longing for family and home into those carols, thinking of her last truly Polish Christmas. The companionship helped to fill the emptiness inside. But only for a while. Once the meal was over, she no longer was able to hold back her depression.

She went back to her dormitory, sat on the floor and pulled her 'new' case from under her bed. It was a rather battered but serviceable item she had managed to buy in the camp shop with the few roubles she earned from her work. She would gain some comfort if she touched the last few memories of Poland held by the items in the case. She would take out her Polish school uniform, fold it neatly and replace it, and then she would look at the family photographs in her tinderbox. She would take her mother's silken shawl from under her pillow and would sniff the faint, lingering remnant of perfume. If she concentrated hard, she would almost imagine herself back in her mother's presence. The routine had comforted her in the past and it would again. She opened the case and reached in.

Her tunic was not there.

Her precious reminder of Poland, and it was gone - the navy school tunic that had been so admired. She closed the case and sat for some time, fighting the intensity of her feelings. One of the Soviet girls had left a few days ago, after finishing her sentence. She had been in her dormitory, and had probably seen the tunic at some time. She would have seen it as something that would make her some money. She must have taken it. Halina lay on her bed and sobbed until it seemed that there was no water left to cry. She would never see her Polish tunic again.

After a long time, her tears gradually subsided and her pride took over. She sat up and dried her face. No one would know she had cried. She would not let them know they had won a battle. At least they had not taken her school coat or the tinderbox. The silver had become so tarnished that they probably thought it a worthless item. Until then, she had tried to be reasonably friendly to the Soviet girls, using the relationship to be subversive when she could, but the experience had shaken her. She would have to be more careful.

The worst of the Soviet girls were from within Russia and many were from the streets of Moscow or Leningrad. They had been thieves, prostitutes or murderers, being younger versions of those who had shared her cell in Homel. There, she had mostly avoided them when she could, preferring to seek out the company of Polish girls in neighbouring cells. In Starodub, she could not avoid them.

The girl in the neighbouring bed to Halina had been a prostitute and the day after Halina had discovered that her case had been looted, Olga came over to Halina. 'I heard you crying last night. Shall I come into your bed tonight?'

'What on earth for?' Halina replied, 'you have got your own bed – sleep in that.' She did not like the look of Olga's ulcers and rashes.

Olga sported several tattoos and cuts on her arm together with ulcers round her mouth. She was always plastered in the make up bought from the shop, and was one of those Halina had seen drinking cologne. Irena, one of the older Polish girls, had told her that Olga had syphilis, like many of the prostitutes, and advised her to keep well away from her in the bathhouse. She had no idea what syphilis was, but it was obviously something to be avoided.

She spoke to Irena about it later that day. 'Olga offered to come into my bed tonight because she thought I needed cheering up. I suppose she was trying to be friendly.'

Irena looked at Halina in amazement, 'You are very naïve, Halina. Do you not know anything about sex? She did not want into your bed just to cheer you up.'

'You are not serious! Sex is between women and men.' Halina flushed with annoyance. How dare Irena call her naïve!

'Don't you listen to those awful songs they sing? They will tell you quite a lot about sex of all kinds. Not to mention what they say when they talk to the education officers.' With that, Irena left, shaking her head at Halina's innocence.

Eugenia had told Halina the basic mechanics of sex when she started her periods at fourteen, and had emphasised the romantic ideal of men and women in love. The poems she had read aloud in prison confirmed this, so the true nature of the relationship between the girls in her dormitory, who shared a bed, was a revelation to Halina. Over the next few days, she paid more attention to the words of the Soviet girls' songs, and gradually began to realise the crudity of the exchanges between the education officers and the girls, especially after she had spoken to Katya.

One evening Halina was sitting in the dormitory trying to work out the meaning of some of the words she had heard the Soviet girls use, when one of the younger girls, originally from Latvia, came up to her and spoke, 'I can tell you what the words mean,' she said.

Halina jumped. She did not realise that she had been saying the words aloud. Katya was about fifteen and very pretty. She had always thought Katya was more innocent than even she was. After all, she had only entered the labour camp a few months previously, having been arrested for crossing the border into Russia. How did she know what the words meant?

'One of the education officers tells me many things. He is very kind to me. Look he gave me this.' Katya showed Halina a pendant she was wearing under her tunic. 'He takes me to his room and says he can help me if I am nice to him.'

Halina could not contain her curiosity any longer and asked Katya, 'But what does he do exactly?' She had to find out what sex was all about. Mama had told her very little detail. She was not going to let Irena patronise her again.

Katya launched into a long discourse giving Halina every detail of what the education officer did to her in his bed. Halina felt her mouth drop open. Was that what really happened? Did men really do that? Surely the education officers should guard the morals of the girls, not corrupt them. Her face turned scarlet as Katya next explained what the words in the Soviet girls' songs meant. Why on earth did they sing songs about it? Did they really want men to do that? After rounding up by explaining all the swear words, Katya scampered off leaving Halina sitting on the floor, stunned into silence. But surely Polish men did not do those things? She tried to remember what Eugenia had told her. The facts seemed to fit, so it must actually be like that.

It took her some time to come to terms with the added knowledge that the education officers seduced the younger girls, but in the end, her increased understanding did nothing to change her romantic ideals. 'Such hypocrisy,' she said to Stasia, as she discussed it with her over lunch that day, 'all the time they say they are here to guide us, and this is what they do. These people know nothing of kindness and decency, so I would expect nothing else from them. For us it will be different.'

Despite her self-righteous words, for the first time she began to understand why her father had been so angry when he had seen her talking to 'strange boys'. Perhaps not all boys were as innocent in their intentions as Edmund. Perhaps even Edmund had not been so innocent.

That night she had a dream about Witold from Homel prison. A dream that made her blush the next day when she remembered it.

Eugenia, December 1940, Siberian Labour Camp

After her near miraculous reprieve, Eugenia tackled her sewing work with alacrity. She knew she was very lucky to be allowed to work inside, and the sewing became a pleasure after the physically punishing work in the forests. It was a miracle she had been selected - any more time in the forest would have killed her. It was a sign that she would survive and find her children. She was sure of it. She looked at the material in front of her. She was sewing winter clothing, which Commander Sulimov had stated that everyone was to have. She had heard some of the guards saying that a recent inspection by his NKVD bosses had been the reason for that.

It was infuriating that she had paid for her clothing, but there was no likelihood of getting her money back. It just showed what a crook he was. Perhaps she should procure some pieces of material to make up for it. When the supervisor was not looking, she might be able to sew some bed covers or clothes for her friends, or patch what they already had. She smiled. That would be a fitting way to get her revenge.

The dramatic improvement in Eugenia's working conditions, contrasted sharply with those of her friends who still worked in the freezing forests. Food rations had improved slightly, but the soup and bread was still inadequate for those whose days were spent in hard physical work. Janka's two remaining daughters seemed most affected, and both developed severe abscesses from lack of vitamin C, although their situation improved a little, when they found some berries growing under some trees they had cut down. Everyone was becoming weaker, and Eugenia worried that they would become as susceptible to illness as she had been.

Two weeks before Christmas, Eugenia returned from work carrying two large parcels she had been told to deliver. One was addressed to Marysia and one to Teresa. Everyone sat and looked in amazement at the parcels, which had postmarks from eastern Poland. Marysia and Teresa opened them to reveal food. Of the many letters sent from the camp, a few had somehow found their way to relatives who had not been arrested or deported themselves. Incredibly, the food parcels they had sent actually arrived, with the promise of more to come.

Marysia spoke first. 'Food. It is actually food. I can't believe it.' She spread out the contents of the parcels. 'Buckwheat, sugar, dried fruit, lard, dried bacon, flour. It is a miracle.'

The arrival of the food parcels was a cause for great celebration, especially as the sharing rule was adhered to, and everyone in their little hut benefited. Eugenia sighed with relief. Now there was a chance everyone would get through the winter.

Twenty Eight

Eugenia, April 1941, Siberian Labour Camp

As she walked back to the hut in early April, after a long day's sewing, Eugenia noticed that it was a little less cold. The worst of winter was nearly over. Once May arrived, things would seem much better. Perhaps the war would soon be over and she would be able to go home. Perhaps she would survive after all. She laughed to herself. She had told herself that so many times. Today she believed it. As she entered the hut smiling, she saw Marysia pacing up and down, a look of terror on her face.

'What is the matter Marysia? You look as if you have seen a ghost.'

Marysia grabbed Eugenia's hand, 'Oh Giena, what will we do. Two of the children I look after have typhus. There is an epidemic in one of the barracks. What if the baby gets it? What if we get it? What can we do?'

Typhus! Eugenia's mood of optimism vanished. In their weakened state, they would have little resistance to the disease and they could die. Children were the most vulnerable.

'We must try harder to clean the hut,' she said, 'Lice carry typhus. You must hope they will allow you to stay in the hut, and not have to look after the children until the danger is over.'

However, the NKVD paid little attention. Those who died were taken away and disinfectant was made available, but still everyone had to work. There was no hospital in the camp; only a few rooms that the doctor used for treating those injured by accidents. Many of the children Marysia looked after became ill and died, but for several weeks, it looked as if the baby and Josef would be saved. However, in the third week of the epidemic, the baby became ill and died very quickly. Then Josef contracted a fever.

Remembering how well she had been looked after when she was ill, Eugenia helped the distraught Marysia with Josef's care. She sponged his forehead as he lay tossing and turning, and tried to get him to drink when he was awake. It was heartbreaking to hear him screaming in pain from the crushing headaches that were a symptom of the disease. She looked at Marysia as she sat exhausted on the floor beside him. How would Marysia cope if she lost Josef as well as the baby? He was so ill there was little chance that he would survive.

For two days, he struggled, but then the inevitable happened. At first, Marysia was almost relieved that her son's life had been extinguished and his pain finally gone, but all too soon grief overwhelmed her. From their little group, five had been lost, Mr and Mrs Pieczko, Vala, the baby, and now Josef.

The snow still lay thick on the ground and a bitter wind blew, when the sad procession of Marysia, Eugenia and their few friends made its way to the clearing in the trees where so many were buried. While Marysia wept her prayers, Eugenia's thoughts turned to her own children. They might have died in the Russian winter. Someone might be burying them. The fear and depression that she had held back for so long, engulfed her, and she wept as much for Halina and Ola as for Josef.

When the group returned to the cabin, she sat on the bunk unable to speak. She had felt for some time that she was in a small boat floating just above the rocks of despair.

She had been kept afloat by the companionship of her friends, her poetry, and the drive to survive so that she would find her daughters again. This latest tragedy had left her stranded, with the rocks in full view.

She was living in hellish conditions. Every day she fought to keep clean, every day she washed and boiled in the endless battle against parasites. Every night she covered her skin to keep out bedbugs, but every morning she woke to find fresh lumps where they had crawled into tiny crevices. The food was dreadful – vile tasting and lacking in nutritional value. Even with the extra food from the parcels, she was always hungry. The dreadful, freezing winter weather sapped her strength. She had even resorted to stealing pieces of cloth.

She lay down on the boards and faced the wall. What if she never left this place? What if she could never leave Russia? She knew she was on the edge of a downward spiral. Once she entered, there would be no return. No amount of poetry would stop it. The fragile optimism between her and despair, had become impossible to maintain. What could save her now?

A summons to the Commandant's office was her salvation.

When she got the message that the Commandant wanted to see her, she started to worry. Would she be taken off sewing and sent back to the forest? What if he had discovered that she sewed clothes for her friends, or worse, that she regularly stole pieces of material? But no. All that happened was she was given a letter and told she should be proud.

She left his office with the letter rustling in her pocket. He had not told her what was in it, but it was obviously something good. She would saviour the anticipation until she had eaten her evening soup and was sitting next to the stove. Everyone watched as she drew the letter from her pocket. She opened it with her hands shaking. It was the first letter she had received since she had arrived at the camp.

To Mrs Eugenia Korbinska
This is to inform you how pleased the authorities at Starodub labour camp are with the conduct of your daughter Halina. She has been seen to work diligently in school and has gained Stakhanoviet status in her work. In particular, her Russian language is very good. As a result, she will be sent to Moscow Medical school to train as a doctor when she reaches seventeen. Comrade Stalin wishes to reward those who are good Soviet citizens. You will be allowed to write to your daughter to tell her.

Halina was alive and well! The news was unexpectedly wonderful and she shared it with everyone in the group. A little of her joy rubbed off on each person she spoke to. After the recent tragic events, even the slightest morsel of good news had the effect of improving morale all round. Even Marysia managed to smile, and that alone, made the rest of the group feel less downhearted.

Eugenia lay awake for some time that night, listening to Monika Reginella snoring quietly. Halina was well. And she must be happy enough if she was working hard in school. It was yet another miracle. Just when she was sure she would die, she had been given the sewing job. Just when despair threatened to overwhelm her, she had received the wonderful news about Halina. Her optimism flared more strongly than ever. Everything would turn out well. She would see her daughters again. This time she would have no doubts.

Twenty Nine

Halina (seated left) in Starodub with 'Anita' (standing) and 'Lucia'.

Halina, May 1941, Starodub Labour Camp

Director Kevich stood at the window watching the girls sitting in the gardens during the lunch break. Such order and good behaviour. And how different from the scene that greeted him when he had arrived eighteen months ago. Then the education officers had been a surly lot who never did what they were told, or did it with bad grace. He puffed his chest out. That was until they met him. He knew how to motivate men. You had to take with one hand and give with the other. Make sure they obeyed the rules and did their job properly. He laughed softly to himself. Of course, he knew that they helped themselves to the young and pretty girls. And who could blame them? However, by turning a blind eye, he had their cooperation. That and the threat of a trip to Siberia. Comrade Stalin knew what he was doing there! Nothing like the threat of Siberia to get them to toe the line.

He turned and sat at his desk. Now this was all his. One of the cushiest labour camps around and it was his. He would not go the way of his predecessor Korallov. He had failed to maintain discipline and look what had happened to him. Vanished. Exiled to one of the harsher camps near Barnaul. No doubt looking for scams anywhere he could. He frowned. He was not at all happy at having to take those Polish madams.

Bad for morale they were. A long way from home and still they made the rest of them look like ignorant peasants. That Anita was a rebellious type. She would come to a bad end some day, if he had anything to do with it. Just let her give him a tiny excuse. He would show her who was in charge. He picked up the letter on his desk. But this letter! One of those Polish girls was to receive such an honour! He did not approve. He did not approve at all. Still.

He tapped his teeth for a moment. But then.... part of the honour would rub off on him. He would go down in history as the one who had tamed a Polish vixen. Perhaps he would even be allowed to meet his hero one day. Imagine if Comrade Stalin came to his camp!

At the beginning of May, Halina was called to the Director's office. She tried hard to think of any misdemeanours that would justify the visit, but could not. She stood in front of his desk apprehensively. What if her sentence was increased? She might not be able to return to Poland for years more.

'I have a letter for you,' said Director Kevich, with what could almost pass for a smile, 'You are to be congratulated.' He passed Halina a letter, which had obviously been opened, and motioned that she could leave.

She waited until she was outside in the garden and on her own before looking at it. Her heart pounded as she examined the writing on the envelope. Surely that was her mother's writing? She stood against a tree looking at the letter for some time, afraid to open it. Perhaps it was not from her, and then she would be bitterly disappointed.

Eventually she opened the flap and took out the letter, noticing that her hand was shaking. She leaned against the tree for support, feeling the rough bark pressing into her back. She turned the letter over to read the ending and sure enough, it was from Eugenia. The letter, written in Russian, was very short and the tone was strangely impersonal. Why had Mama not written with more love and told her more about what she was doing? She thought for a few moments. Of course! The letter had been read by the director of the labour camp and probably by many officials before him, so Mama would have realised she would have to be careful what she wrote.

My Dear Halina,
I hope you are well. I have been working in a Siberian forest cutting trees since you left. However, I became ill and too weak to work, but I was fortunate in being allowed to move to another facility as a concession, where I started sewing work. I am now much better.

Her beautiful, elegant mother out in the icy weather cutting trees! No wonder she became ill.

I have heard from the authorities in Moscow. They are very pleased with how hard you work and how well you are doing in school and have decided to award you a great honour. When you are seventeen, you are to leave the labour camp and go to university in Moscow to train as a doctor.
All my love,
Your loving mother,
Eugenia Korbinska

132

Halina read the letter over and over again. It was so wonderful to hear from Mama. She had been so upset when Ola had been taken away, and all this time she had been worrying she would lose her mind when both her daughters had gone, but somehow she had coped. Halina did not know whether to laugh or cry - she had forgotten what being happy was like. She read the letter again. What was more, Mama had an inside job sewing. Halina smiled at that. To think they were both sewing! Every time she threaded a needle now, she would think of her doing the same, somewhere on the other side of Russia. It would be a link between them.

Thoughts rushed uncontrolled around her head. Thank God she was not outside in the Siberian winter. And she was well. Surely she would see her again when the war was over. Halina danced a little round the tree, finding it difficult to contain her excitement. Then she stopped short and read the end of the letter again. Go to Moscow medical school? She might never be allowed to leave Russia. Some of the Soviet girls had made it clear that no one could leave Russia without permission. A qualified doctor would never be allowed to leave. She stood, stunned by the thought. To have found Mama just to lose her again? What if she was not allowed to see her? What if she never saw her again? Then she remembered. She would be seventeen in two months time.

June 1941

Some weeks after Halina had received the letter from her mother, the camp director stood up to address the camp, which was assembled for the evening lecture. 'Tonight you are to see a film about Poland as it was before the glorious Red Army liberated the peasants.' As he spoke, he smiled triumphantly at the Polish group.

Halina looked at Lucia who was sitting next to her, 'I don't like the sound of this,' she said apprehensively.

The film was far worse than anything she could have imagined. It was the worse kind of propaganda and painted a picture of a nation of peasants and workers who lived in terror of the Polish lords and officers who beat them and ill-treated them. The film concluded by saying how grateful the peasants were to the Red Army when they liberated them.

Halina sat burning with fury. How could they tell such terrible lies! Her father always treated his soldiers well and they had great respect for him. What about the dreadful things the NKVD had done to decent people? She dug her fingers into her hand so hard that her nails cut the skin. She looked across at Lucia and saw that she had tears running down her face, but she made no sound. As the film finished there was a palpable feeling of hostility in the room, and the Soviet girls turned to look in the direction of the Polish group. Anita stood up and shouted, 'It is all lies. Don't believe such rubbish.' At that, she turned and stormed out of the room with all eyes on her.

Halina sat silently with the other Polish girls, as the Soviet girls filed out glaring at them and showering them with curses as they went. When the room was empty, she got up and walked along the corridor with Lucia. Neither of them said a word on route to their dormitory, too upset by what they had seen. As she entered the dormitory, Halina became nervous. What if the Soviet girls in the room were hostile? She had always tried to appear friendly to them, but who knows how they would react to the film. As she walked in, the girls said nothing. Perhaps she would be safe after all. After a long silence, her neighbour Olga turned to her and spoke, 'You poor girls, what a terrible country you lived in. What about all those stories you told us about your wonderful life in Poland. They were just lies to hide your shame.'

Halina lay down on her bed and tried hard not to cry. She did not like being in the position of the underdog. So much for their subversion. All their hard work had gone for nothing, because of one film.

Next day there was less overt hostility, but the atmosphere in the camp had changed and Halina felt vulnerable for the first time since her arrest. She noticed that Anita was absent and asked Irena if she had seen her.

'She was taken to the director's office for shouting after the film,' Irena told her, 'I keep telling her she should be careful what she says, but she will not listen. Let's hope things settle down soon.'

However, things did not settle down. A few days later, Germany declared war on the Soviet Union and the Polish group took on the role of scapegoat.

Thirty

Halina, July 1941, Starodub Labour Camp

Halina heard the news while in a lesson with Maria. The director came into the classroom and made the announcement. She was exultant; perhaps this would be the end of the Soviets! However, she dare not show too much in her face. She looked down at the table to disguise her pleasure. When he had gone, Maria talked quietly to the Polish group and warned them to be careful what they said.

'They are watching you carefully, girls. If you say anything careless about Germany attacking Soviet Russia it will not go well for you.'

In the dining hall that evening, Halina could see panic in the faces of the Soviet girls. They had been told so often about the superiority of the Soviet system that the thought of being attacked by another country terrified them. She looked at the meagre amount on her plate. The food had been greatly reduced in quality and quantity. Was that just the Polish girls or was everyone in the same situation? After the meal, she walked out into the garden with Stasia, and they heard the distant sound of explosions.

'The Germans are coming,' Stasia said, 'Perhaps we will be freed and will be able to return to Poland.'

Halina was about to answer her when she noticed Anita lying on the grass. She rushed over and saw that she had blood on her face. Together she and Stasia lifted Anita up and supported her as they walked her back to her dormitory.

'They attacked me,' she whispered, 'the Soviet girls attacked me when I was walking in the garden. All I said was that Germany might defeat them. I just told the truth.'

Halina and Stasia helped to clean the blood off Anita's face and waited with her until she fell asleep. Halina was reluctant to go to the evening meeting. She did not like the way the atmosphere had changed since that dreadful film. Now that Germany had declared war, the atmosphere had become even worse. She sat down next to Stasia and looked around apprehensively. The Soviet girls shouted comments at them and called them German sympathisers. The girls sitting behind her pulled her hair very hard and another girl hit Stasia in the head. What would they do next?

The hostility in the room grew more vocal, and the insults grew louder and wilder. Halina became even more fearful. The education officers ran up and down trying to calm everyone, but only succeeded after they started singing the Russian national anthem, the Internationale, in an attempt to create calm. Gradually the room subsided as patriotism took a more constructive form. Halina kept her mouth closed. Usually she mimed to the song, but tonight she would not even do that.

Went she went to bed after the meeting, Halina lay for some time unable to sleep. What if the Soviet girls continued their hostility? They might attack her as she slept. She put her hand under the pillow to take out her mother's silken shawl and looked at in dismay. It had been cut into shreds. The Soviet girls had taken their revenge. She wished they had pulled her hair or made abusive remarks. That she could stand. But not Mama's shawl. How could they rip up something that meant so much to her? Of course, that was why they did it. They knew exactly how important it was to her.

She squeezed the shawl into a ball and held it to her nose. The perfume had faded and all that was left was a memory.

The next day at lunch, Halina and her group sat eating quietly, hoping they would not be subjected to more verbal abuse. The food they had enjoyed for months had been replaced with a thin gruel and a very small portion of black bread. She was about to complain when she realised that Anita, Irena and another two girls were missing. 'They were called to the director's office this morning,' Stasia whispered, 'I am afraid for them.'

For days the girls were not seen, promoting rumours of where they had gone and what had been said to them.

'Those traitorous friends of yours are in prison and will be shot,' one of the worst of the Soviet girls leaned over and whispered in Halina's ear. The girl, Lola, had been sent to the labour camp for murdering and robbing two women, and was someone Halina tried to avoid. She said nothing and turned away as if the comment had meant nothing, but inside she felt small stabs of panic.

After a week, Anita, Irena and the other girls returned. They looked very pale and their faces were full of strain. There was little opportunity during the day to speak to them, but Halina and Stasia managed to find Irena alone in her dormitory before the evening lecture.

'They put us in cells,' Irena said, her voice trembling, 'They were no worse than prison cells, but the directors interrogated us day and night. They said we were agitators and German sympathisers and spent our time trying to demoralise the Soviet girls. They accused us of saying all kinds of things. We were so afraid they were going to beat us, or worse. Then they said we were to be sentenced. I think they are going to shoot us.'

The words sent a chill through Halina. They were so vulnerable in the camp and now it seems they were to be victimised.

'What if one of the Soviet girls takes it into her head to kill us,' said Stasia, chewing her nail as she spoke. 'Several have already murdered and they might be excused for choosing us as their next victims.'

'Let us just hope the Germans free us before things get worse,' Halina replied calmly. She would not let the others know that she was just as frightened as they were.

Whether the threats to Irena and the others were really going to take place, or whether it had been propaganda designed to frighten them into submission, the events of the following days changed everything. Bombs started falling near Starodub.

Halina and her friends remained calm, delighting in the panic around them and believing that they would soon be freed. The frightening events of the previous weeks were forgotten, as once again they felt secure. All around the Soviet girls looked white and terrified and forgot to persecute the Polish group.

After a few days, the camp director called a meeting in the lecture hall and stood on the stage. 'Tonight the camp is being evacuated. We are travelling over the Ural Mountains to an adult labour camp in Siberia. You must pack your belongings and be ready to leave in two hours.'

Halina was overjoyed. Her mother was in Siberia. She might be able to see her again.

'It will be wonderful to be treated like adults,' said Stasia, 'and get away from here.'

Three hours later Halina was still waiting with her group. Most of the rest of the camp had been evacuated. 'Perhaps they are leaving us behind,' Stasia said, 'or perhaps they will shoot us before they go,' she added, turning white at the thought.

Eventually the only Soviet girls left were Lola and her group – the worst of the criminals in the camp. The Polish group joined them and together they marched to the station. It was so different from the day Halina had arrived – this time she had her Polish companions for support and the hope that she might see her mother again. Her case was much heavier than when she came, as she had managed to accumulate a few possessions in her time in the labour camp, but she hardly noticed the extra weight. As the group passed through the streets, crude comments were shouted at the Soviet girls, who replied with rude signs and ruder replies, then Halina saw an old woman watching them. As they approached she spoke, 'Have courage, sisters. It is you today and me tomorrow.' Halina was confused. Did the Soviets send their own people to Siberia?

They arrived at the station to find a long train with about thirteen or fourteen cattle trucks waiting for them, and they were herded into the last carriage. Halina looked around apprehensively. It was very like the truck she had travelled in to Homel. She relaxed a little. At least this one was clean. She recognised the hole in the middle of the carriage as being the toilet, but this one had a rigid barrier round it. That was a relief. She had become used to some privacy and did not fancy the alternative. There were bunks at the end, which the education officer and the guards commandeered, leaving the girls with the hard wooden floor to sit on. Halina glowered at them. Trust them to take the best position.

The education officer stood up and announced how he expected them to behave. 'We will get food and water at the stations on the way,' he said, 'but we will use the stove when required. We will also stop at stations so that you can wash and relieve yourself, but the hole in the floor can be used at other times. We have erected a barrier round it to preserve your modesty. The journey is expected to take a month, but we will stop on the way to allow you some exercise. Your lessons will continue when possible. We will continue to tell you the history of the glorious revolution and the triumphs of our great leader Stalin against the German hordes.'

Halina just avoided smirking. He would find it difficult to talk about great triumphs when they were all running away from the German hordes. Then her face fell as she looked around. She would have to spend a month in the wagon in close proximity with some of the worst of the Russian girls and the guards. That dampened her enthusiasm somewhat.

As the train started moving and the rattling sound of the trucks filled the space, Halina sat on her case with her back against the truck side and tried to work out how she felt about the move. It was disappointing not to have been left behind and rescued by the Germans, but then there was no guarantee they would have been treated any better by the Germans - the Poles were their enemies too after all. However, she was going towards her mother, and there was always the chance she would see her again. That was worth far more. But Russia was a big place. She might never find her. She smiled to herself. Of course she would find her. She was sure of it. She closed her eyes, and lulled by the swaying of the carriage she fell asleep.

The first week of the journey was a novelty to be enjoyed. There was sufficient food, either cooked on the stove, or obtained at one of the stations at which they stopped, and a reasonable supply of water. The carriage became hot as the sun heated it, but the train stopped regularly and the doors were opened to let in cooler air. At stations, they were allowed to wash using water from the pumps, and once or twice when the train stopped, they were allowed outside to walk around. Morning and afternoon, they were given lessons, mostly propaganda, but they were allowed to sing songs, even if they mainly consisted of hymns praising Stalin. In the evenings, the Polish group talked of home and family, of pleasures lost, and wishes for the future. Gradually the boredom of the journey drained away Halina's enthusiasm, and she became stiff from inactivity, both mental and physical. Only the occasional stops gave relief from the monotony.

After days of unrelenting tedium, the train started to cross the Ural Mountains. The views were spectacular but the train only stopped briefly at stations, spending its time climbing the inclines at a snail's pace. Halina groaned with boredom. The slowness with which they covered ground was intensely frustrating. She had never seen such large forests, swamps and rivers. Would they ever arrive? Eventually the train pulled to a halt in what seemed to be the middle of nowhere. The door was opened and everyone was told to get out. Previous stops had been short, with little opportunity for more than the minimum of exercise, but this time they were told the stop would be for several hours. Halina leapt up with enthusiasm. A chance to walk outside was not to be missed.

In front was a wonderful sight. As far as she could see stretching to the horizon, was a vast grassy plain. It was mainly flat, but with low rolling hills here and there, and unlike anything she had seen before. She had heard of the Russian Steppes in geography lessons, but nothing prepared her for all that space and the vastness of the blue sky. It was spellbinding. She sat down on the grass with the others and started picking the wild flowers that grew around in profusion. It was like being back in the Carpathians on her family holidays. If she made some garlands, she would have something to remind her of those times. She lay back in the grass. The sun was warm and a slight breeze ruffled her air. If she closed her eyes, she might see images of Ola and her family.

Someone shouted and brought her back to earth and she opened her eyes. She had almost imagined Ola and Mama were with her. That must explain why she felt happier than she had for a long time. She looked around her, hungry for the sight of space. With the train behind her back and vast acres of grassy plain in front of her, it felt like freedom. She stood up again and started to walk across the grass. There were so many people in the field she was able to walk some distance without leaving the group. Perhaps she should start running and keep running to freedom. However, there was nowhere to run to, just more and more grass. When eventually she had to board the train, she felt as if the burden of months of imprisonment had been lifted. She would never forget the ecstasy of being on the edge of freedom. She held the garland to her nose. Each time she smelled the flowers she would remember.

138

Thirty One

Halina, August 1941, Barnaul Labour Camp

Finally, the train stopped and did not move off again. The door was pulled aside and Halina sat blinking in the bright light.

'Time to get out. This is Barnaul,' the guard said, waving his gun. Halina rose to her feet slowly, stiff and sore in every limb after the weeks of enforced inactivity. She was hot, hungry and thirsty, but most of all she felt dirty. Her clothes stuck to her in sweaty, smelly lumps, her underwear chafed and rubbed. However, she did not want to think too closely about that. She longed for some cold water. They had not stopped at a station to wash for two days and the drinking water carried in the train had become warm in the heat of the truck. Halina picked up her little suitcase. It was even more battered and scratched than when she bought it, but she held it close. It contained all that she owned in the world - all that had not been stolen, worn out or thrown away. It was all she had. Only a small suitcase with some clothes, some soap, a comb and her tinderbox. However, she had her friends still. The Polish spirit had been stifled in the heat of the cattle truck, but now it would be revived again.

It was disappointing that Russia was so large. She had hoped that she might meet her mother in Siberia, but she had not bargained for the huge size of the country. It had taken the train a month to travel to Barnaul from Starodub. What chance would there be of finding Mama? She stumbled to the door, climbed down from the train and made her way to the station. There were several hundred girls and insufficient transport to take them to the labour camp, so they had to wait for several hours until a lorry was available, but the time passed quickly and at last, one came. Halina climbed aboard. She was feeling cheerful and optimistic again.

As he watched the last of the transport leave, Director Kevich scowled and took the letter out of his pocket. It had been sent ahead to this final station with his other mail. The camp inmates had arrived safely, now he could travel on at his leisure. He re-read the letter. There it was in black and white. There had been an agreement between the Soviet government and the Polish government-in-exile in Britain. The Polish girls could be set free. Those little vixens! He could not understand it. How could they let them free? But no need to rush with the news. Let those little Polish madams find out later. If he knew anything, Korallov would not be in any hurry to lose his work force. His scowl deepened. Now that Germany had invaded, he had lost his cushy post at Starodub. What was worse he would have to meet that worm Korallov and watch him smirking when he told him. With that, he folded the letter, put it back in his pocket and walked towards the car waiting for him. It was a black day.

After half an hour of being thrown from side to side, as the wagon lurched over the ruts and holes in the road, the group finally arrived at its destination. Halina climbed out of the wagon eagerly. Now there would be beds, water to bathe in, food and drink. The thought of a meal such as regularly eaten in Starodub made her mouth water. She stood and looked around in dismay. There were no old garden walls, no gardens and trees, no large stone buildings. All she could see was a wire fence topped with barbed wire. There were wooden towers at intervals along the length of the wire, and in the top of each, there was a guard. Each guard was holding a gun. Halina passed through the gate. In front of her was a large compound with rows of long wooden barracks leading to another row at right angles. The whole of the compound was enclosed by wire fencing with more guard towers. From a hut near the gate came the sound of barking. Dogs! She heard one of the guards say that they kept the dogs hungry just in case anyone tried to escape. She hoped it was not true. However, there was a bigger problem. They were the last group to arrive and that meant they would have the worst of the accommodation. The guards pushed her towards a hut at the end of the line. Now it seemed that they would have to share it with Lola the murderess and her group - the most amoral of the thieves and criminals who had been in Starodub.

Halina pushed through the door of the barracks and stood in shock. She had expected some kind of dormitory. Not this. The building consisted of a long high hall with rows of wide shelves, covered in what looked like rags, on each side. She looked more closely. She was horribly wrong. The shelves were beds and the rags were people. This was worse than prison. At either end of the building was a large round stove with a pipe rising up through the roof. The walls were wooden with moss packed between the timbers. It was cold and damp inside and it was only August. What would it be like in winter?

One of the Soviet girls came up and told Halina and her group that they had to find a corner for themselves with a bed. She looked around, but there was no space. The girls who had just entered now took up whatever space there had been. She looked over and saw Lola pushing people out of the way and threatening them if they objected. Her companions were following suite. She was not going to sink to their level. She and her friends would have to try to squeeze in where they could.

Eventually they managed to find a corner with cracked wooden boards. It was near the stove, which meant some warmth, but the air was smoky and became smokier each time fuel was added.

'There are no blankets,' cried Stasia. She turned and asked a woman standing at the stove where they could get blankets.

The woman turned her face towards them, and Halina was shocked by her appearance. She was very thin, and filthy. Her clothes had been good quality once, but now were covered with dried grey mud. And her expression! Her eyes had such a haunted look in them it was chilling just to look at her. Her face was drawn and there were black circles under her eyes. 'Blankets?' she said, 'There are no blankets. You have to use your clothes.' With that, she turned and walked away.

Halina was disappointed. She would have liked to talk to another Polish inmate, but the fact that she had arrived with an aggressive Russian group seemed to have branded her as someone to be avoided.

She took some clothes out of her case and laid them on the boards.

'My God,' Stasia shrieked.

'What is it?' Halina turned to see what Stasia was looking at.

Lice. Hundreds of them. Crawling everywhere on the boards, on the walls, but most of all on the barracks' inmates. Halina's scalp started to crawl. It was worse than Homel prison. With this number, they would have to work hard to keep clean. She watched Lola and her gang continuing to push their way into the throng near the wooden boards. Lice would not be the only problem. It looked like it would be everyone for themselves.

An hour later Halina had found out where the latrines were, and Stasia had found a pot from somewhere- she did not say where- and set about washing their dirty clothes. Lucia had even erected a barrier with some clothes so that they could have some privacy to wash. Halina hung their washing over the sides of the wooden frames round the beds. She sat on her corner of the wooden board, thoughtfully chewing the last few remnants of bread she had saved, then, exhausted, she lay down with her head on her case, and slept.

She awoke what seemed like a few minutes later. Someone was crying in one corner of the room and the sound of retching and coughing came from another. She rolled over and put her fingers in her ears. She did not want to have to listen to that unpleasant sound. Soon exhaustion won out and she fell asleep again, this time for longer.

She woke several times in the night, unaccustomed to the hard boards and the movements of those around her. The clothes on which she lay had turned with her in the night, and were now heaped in uncomfortable lumps. She could not stop thinking about her arrival. The 'greeting' from the camp commandant had been very different from that in Starodub. There she had been told she would be well treated if she worked hard, and there had been some kindness, albeit mostly from Maria. The atmosphere here was very different. The commandant had been severe and unsmiling. 'You will start work at seven,' he had said, 'If you work you will be given food. You must work. If you do not work you will not eat and you will die.' So much for being treated like an adult. It seemed as if they were to be treated like slaves. She closed her eyes again. Perhaps things would seem better in the morning.

They were woken at seven by the sound of metal striking metal – their signal to get up. Halina absently scratched her ankle and looked down to see a large red lump. There were more on her legs and hands and round her neck. They did not look like fleabites and the lump was much larger than anything a louse could produce.

'I am covered in lumps,' grumbled Stasia.

Lucia was more knowledgeable. 'I think they are bed bug bites. I had one once when I stayed with someone from school. My mother did not let me go to her house again.'

Halina hastily ate the bread she had just been given and washed it down with hot water. The bread was black, hard and unpleasant but it was all they had been given. She had to get to work quickly. She had to impress the NKVD and gain the Stakhanoviet title she had in Starodub. Perhaps then she would be given decent food and quarters without parasites.

There was very little time to eat the bread before the group had to go to roll call. Halina joined the end of a row and looked around. Most of the group from Starodub were together, but she could see rows of faces behind that she did not recognise. They stood obediently in their rows without speaking until the counting of heads had finished. An NKVD official came to speak to the group from Starodub. There was nearly a whole carriage load in Halina's barracks squeezed in between the original occupants. 'You will work in the brick making area,' he said, 'you must come now.'

They were marched out of the gate. There were about fifty in the group, and they walked four abreast along the track. Guards accompanied them with dogs trotting alongside. They were fierce-looking beasts who looked half-starved. Halina put her hands in her pockets. They just might take a fancy to her fingers. They walked over rough, rutted ground for about a mile. There were trees all around and fields of poor-looking soil where the ground was reasonably level.

Here and there were signs of habitation with small wooden houses dotted about. There were tall posts at intervals along the road, with the tops painted a faded red. It took Halina a few minutes to work out what they were. Of course! The posts were there to mark the position of the road when covered in snow. She had seen similar posts in the Carpathian Mountains. Did the snow really get so deep here?

The guards walked at a fast pace and she had to trot to keep up. There had been too many weeks of inactivity. They came to a gate into a large field and walked in. In the field, there were several large circles, each about a foot deep. The Russian girl next to her said, 'Bricks. We are making bricks.'

Halina had no knowledge of how bricks were made, but did not expect to be told to remove her boots. 'If you leave them on they will be ruined in no time,' said her neighbour, 'My mother used to make bricks at the farm. My family could not afford to buy them.'

A group of women came from the other side of the field carrying piles of straw and threw the straw into the pit. Another group poured in water. As she looked over the edge, Halina could see grey mud at the bottom under the straw. One of the guards addressed her group.

'You are to make bricks. You will walk round in the hole to mix the clay with the straw and water. When it is of the correct consistency, you will put the mixture into wooden formers,' he picked one up to show to them, 'and leave them to dry in the sun.' He repeated what they had been told the night before. 'You must work to eat. If you do not work, you will not eat.'

Halina moved forward and stepped into the hole. The clay was cold and slippery and the straw rough. The guard shouted at them to start moving. Now she had to start walking round in circles. It was difficult to keep her feet and almost immediately, she slipped and fell. She stood up shakily. Her coat was covered with sticky grey mud. Her Polish school coat that had spent over a year folded in her case and was almost clean. She was only here for a day and now it was filthy. The guard shouted curses at her and she found it difficult to keep her mouth shut. What was the point of learning all those Russian swear words from listening to the Soviet girls if she could not use them! But she must not fall again. She would just have to concentrate harder.

After a while, she was relieved to find that her balance improved, and she was able to tread without slipping. Perhaps she might manage to keep her coat clean after all. The clay sucked at her feet as she lifted them up. It was such exhausting work pulling them out again.

There was a brief break in the middle of the day, when the group received hot water with something floating in it. Halina looked at it. Was it soup or tea? It was difficult to tell from the taste. She longed for more food. Her stomach ached from hunger. The more she walked, the hungrier she became. She had been walking for hours round and round like a horse, her back bent as she leaned forward to keep her balance. She found it difficult to contain her anger. How dare they treat her this way! It was humiliating. Her legs ached and the mud had spread up her legs and over her clothes. No wonder

142

the women in the camp looked so dirty. How would she manage to keep clean if she had to do this every day?

One of the camp officials came over and she asked him how much she had to do to become a Stakhanoviet worker. She had been treated reasonably well in Starodub until Germany attacked the Soviets. Surely it would be the same here?

'Just work as hard as you can,' he snarled at her, 'and don't waste time asking questions.' She had to start walking round in circles again.

At some stage in the afternoon, they stopped walking round, and were told to empty out the bricks, which had dried in the sun from the previous day. Then they had to pack the clay mixture into the wooden formers. Halina looked around but there were no tools. She would have to lift up the mixture by hand and press it in. Her hands and arms became covered with the mixture, so that by the end of the day, there were few areas on her body not covered with the grey sticky mess. She would have to scrub for ages to get clean.

As they walked back to the camp after working until six, Halina caught up with Stasia, Lucia, and some of the other girls. They looked as tired as she did. 'They don't seem to bother about Stakhanoviet here,' Lucia said, looking very miserable 'I don't know how we can improve our conditions otherwise.'

Halina put her arm round her, 'Don't worry, Lucia. We will just have to try and make the best of things.' The walk seemed to take twice as long going back as it had coming, but at least there was the possibility of food at the end of the walk.

On return to the camp, Stasia fetched water from the pump and they put it in a pot to heat on one of the stoves. Halina tried to sponge the worst of the mud off her coat. She could not let her school coat be ruined. It was the only good item of clothing she had. The other women from the barracks came back, having taken much longer to return. Halina watched them drag their way back. They looked even more exhausted than she did. She tried to speak to one or two, but they ignored her. That was Lola's fault. The behaviour of the Russian group had caused so much resentment that they would not speak to her. The situation was made worse when they queued up for soup in the camp kitchen. The Russian girls had made sure they were at the front of the queue, and the sudden increase in numbers due to the influx from Starodub, meant there was not enough to go round.

Halina looked at the thin evil-smelling liquid in her bowl. Perhaps she should share it with one of those who had missed out. The thought only passed quickly through her mind. She was too hungry. Out of the corner of her eye, she saw one of Lola's gang grab the soup bowl from a woman who offered no resistance. Instinctively the Polish group moved closer together. There was no doubt that here the Soviet girls were in charge. They would have to be careful.

Thirty Two

Eugenia, September 1941, Siberian Labour Camp

By July, news had filtered into the camp that Germany had declared war on Soviet Russia. The news was very exciting, and Eugenia felt that at last they would be saved. But the euphoria did not last. Soon afterwards, the food parcels stopped, and the food in the camp became worse than ever. The food from previous parcels was carefully husbanded to last as long as possible, and Eugenia worked harder than ever to try to earn more bread for the group, but as August wore on, the future began to look bleak.

She looked at the small store of food in the hut. Once the food from the parcels had gone, they would not have enough. She felt a sudden prick of fear. A few more months and they would be facing starvation. She just had to hope that something would turn up. Surely she had not survived so long for nothing. So many had died in the camp. At first it was those who had not brought extra food with them, then others succumbed to the freezing winter, and finally typhus took many more lives. She had survived so long she could not bear the thought that she would lose the final battle. The only hope she had left was that the war with Germany would somehow offer a lifeline. And so it did.

At the end of August, Commandant Sulimov announced that there had been an agreement signed with the Polish government–in–exile and all Polish prisoners were free to go. There was to be a Polish army formed in Uzbekistan near Tashkent. When she first heard the news, Eugenia felt the blood rush from her head and she had to sit down quickly before she fainted. She could go home. She could actually go home! She could look for the girls and Kazimierz, and could start to live again. Two years of worry and torment were over. She did not know how to express her feelings. The news was just so overwhelming.

The whole camp was in a state of high excitement, and people previously exhausted and morose, suddenly came to life with energy they did not know they had. Mrs Reginella helped them to keep their feet on the ground. 'We must prepare for the journey. We must have food and water on the way and we do not know how long we will be travelling. We have to get to the nearest station first and that is at least two days walk away, so we may need to take items to sell to the Russians if we encounter any. None of us is strong. To make sure we arrive at all, we must plan.'

They had to wait several, interminable, days for the arrival of their amnesty paperwork, which guaranteed them free passage, and finally they were ready to leave. They divided the remaining food so that everyone had a share of bread and dried fruit. The fruit had come in Teresa's last food parcel and she had kept it 'for emergencies'. The two kilograms did not go far when shared among the group, but it was such a luxury it seemed much more to everyone. The Commandant offered transport to take groups to the station, but for this, they had to pay. 'We will need all we have for food,' Janka said, 'and two days walk to the station is not that much. Beside, I do not trust

Commandant Sulimov. Who knows where he will take us.'

In the end, only Mrs Reginella from their group took up the offer. 'I could not walk that distance,' she explained, 'You will know which train I have gone in because I will ask someone to hang my Polish flag on the back.' At this, she pulled a flag out of her bag. 'I have had this next to my heart ever since we came here, but that is a better use for it.'

As the wagons pulled out of the camp, Eugenia followed behind with Marysia, Teresa, Janka and her two daughters. Sabina and Karolina had decided to walk with friends they had made in their work group, and were some distance in front. Her heart was full and she could hardly speak. Perhaps if she sang Polish hymns and folksongs everyone would join in. That would be a good way to pass the time. They had two days walking ahead, after all. Soon she had the whole group singing the Polish National Anthem.

It was late afternoon before they came upon any habitation – a small village attached to a communal farm. As Eugenia could speak Russian, she was designated to speak for her friends. She went up to an old woman who was carrying wood to her small wooden cottage. 'We are Poles and have been freed from the labour camp. Can we stay here for the night? We can pay.'

The old woman looked at her for some time then nodded. She took in Eugenia and Teresa and indicated several houses where the others might find a space. That night, after a meal of soup and bread, Eugenia lay on the earth floor of the cottage in front of the stove, warm and content. She had been shocked by the poverty in the houses round about. The conditions were similar to those in their hut in the camp. There was a bucket behind a screen for a toilet, light was from a battered oil lamp and the surroundings were none too clean. Despite that, the old woman had been friendly and had listened with interest to her stories of life in Poland.

They had paid for the hospitality with clothing, some of which she had stolen from the sewing room hidden under her tunic on her last day of work. She smiled to herself as she thought of the thieves in the prison in Homel. What would they think of her now! She began to understand a little of what had driven them to a life of crime. If you had nothing, stealing from an enemy was a natural act. She simply had a different definition from those Russian thieves of who the enemy was.

In the morning, Marysia came up to Eugenia smiling - the first time she had smiled for months. 'I have given all of Josef's clothes to a young couple, and they will take us to the station in their cart. It will save us a whole day.'

A few hours later, they arrived at the station, which they had first seen a year before. There was only one person around, and Eugenia was surprised to see it was Sabina. 'Where is everyone else, Sabina? Why are you still here?'

'Oh, thank God. I am so pleased to see you.' Sabina was standing outside the station building and it was obvious she had been crying. Next to her was a large pot of soup. 'We had to wait until this morning for the train and when it arrived it was almost full of prisoners from a camp further north. We all had to squeeze in to get on the train, packed like sardines in the wagons. Then someone said there was soup in the station, so I got out with the pot to get soup for us all, but the train started moving before I could get back. I screamed at the driver to stop and ran alongside waving my arms, but he just ignored me. All I could see was the little Polish flag that Mrs Reginella had hung out of the grille on the top of the last truck. Thank goodness you are here.' She looked a little sheepish at her display of emotion, and added, 'Well at least I have some soup for you, though it is a bit cold now.'

The soup was more welcome than anyone could have imagined, as there was no train for a day and a half. The excitement of being free was still coursing in Eugenia's veins and she spent much of the time pacing up and down with frustration. Would they ever leave this place? Still, they were fortunate in that the station had a plentiful supply of soup and bread, and she comforted herself with the thought that if they had walked all the way, they would only just have arrived.

At last, their patience was rewarded, and a train pulled in with several cattle trucks attached to the back. The sight of a cattle truck gave Eugenia a stab of fear as she remembered her previous journeys, but this time they would not be under guard and would be able to leave the doors open if they wished. The train travelled very slowly, and Eugenia was glad, not for the first time, that she could speak Russian. It made it so much easier to get information and meant she could read the train routes and timetables. The train stopped several times on the way, and they managed to get water and food each time, but their supply of items to sell was shrinking rapidly and there was still a long way to go.

Finally, they arrived at the station where they had to change trains for Tashkent. It was a large station where several main lines met, close to Novosibirsk. Little did Eugenia guess that Halina was still in her labour camp less than a hundred miles away. As she got down from the train, she noticed that there was another train parked in a siding, but it was the sight on the station that shocked her. The station itself was a sea of faces. There were people sitting, people standing, people lying down. They looked thin, exhausted, and filthy, but amongst them was a tattered Polish army uniform. She had not seen a Polish uniform for so long that she was drawn towards it.

As she drew nearer, she noticed that the wearer was a pitiable sight. His face was so thin, the skull bones were clearly defined and his uniform hung like rags on a scarecrow. He was completely covered in lice; something that at one time would have disgusted her, but now she hardly noticed. She had to speak to him. Perhaps he knew Kazimierz. She went up to him and found out he had been released from prison and had just arrived. 'I have nothing,' he said, 'I have to rely on others for food.' Despite his condition, he managed to smile. Her heart went out to him. He was only about nineteen.

Without hesitating, she went into her bag and brought out Ola's socks. They were her last link to Ola, but the soldier needed them more than her. 'Take these,' she said, 'They are made from good quality wool so there should be enough to trade for some food.' The soldier took them without a moment's hesitation and pushed his way unsteadily through the throng towards the station building.

As Eugenia looked around, she saw several NKVD men and immediately felt alarmed. 'Janka,' she said, 'look at those men. Why are they here?'

'I have been speaking to those women over there,' Janka replied, indicating a group near the station building, 'It seems that the train in the siding has been quarantined – there is typhus on board. The NVKD are here to stop anyone from leaving the train, even if they are well. All they are doing is passing up water and food via a bucket and rope.' As she looked, Eugenia saw that there were large containers on the other side of the train. One of the doors opened and a body was thrown into one of the containers.

Just as she turned away, she noticed something. 'Sabina, look, is that a Polish flag on the outside of the train?'

Sabina looked to where Eugenia was pointing. 'Oh no! I think it is Mrs Reginella's flag. Is this the train that the people from our camp took? Is it the one that I missed? My sister is on that train.'

Eugenia managed to find a railway worker who was standing by, looking confused and obviously not sure what to do with the hordes of refugees on his station. 'Do you know where that train has come from?' she asked.

'That is the only other train that has come through here for three days.' The man pointed to the map on the side of the station building, 'It came from further north.' The station worker told her there was a train due the next day. 'They will probably put more carriages on to get everyone away from here. It is chaos. How can we do our job with all these people?'

'It must be the same train, Sabina. That must be Mrs Reginella's flag.' Eugenia could feel the blood draining from her face. They had come so close to getting on that train. Were it not for Janka's insistence on walking, they might all be trapped in it.

She pushed the hair from her face. What had happened to her? At one time the thought of a whole train full of people trapped inside, surrounded by sickness and death would have struck her to the core. She recalled her reaction to the deportations in Luck and realised just how inured she had become to the suffering of others. Throughout her captivity, she had battled to maintain her mental strength and in doing so, her emotions had become dulled: now she saw illness as a fact of life, death the unfortunate result.

She glanced once more in the direction of the train. She should be feeling the pain of those suffering on the train, not simply feeling thankful it was not her. She moved towards Sabina who needed her support. The Soviets had taken so much from her but she would not allow them to take her humanity.

That night they had no choice but to sleep on the station like the hundreds of others around. Sabina had tried to move closer to the quarantined train, but was prevented by an NKVD officer who pointed his gun at her. 'My sister is on that train, please let me past,' she implored, but to no avail. She dissolved into floods of tears and the others tried to comfort her, reminding her that Karolina had survived the typhus epidemic in the camp and that she might be safe. She insisted that she would stay and wait for the chance to contact those on board.

Eugenia and her little group stayed at the edge of the throng. Too many looked diseased and louse-ridden and Teresa announced she had seen some people stealing. Everyone exhibited the frustration and desperation that Eugenia had felt when waiting at the first station. The groups had come from all directions, like rivers flowing to the sea, and they were determined, desperate even, to leave.

They had to wait two days for the train. Two days in which they had to fight to get water and food. Two days in which the filth accumulated and the parasites multiplied, but two days nearer to freedom. When the train finally came, there was a stampede to get on board. In the end, the NKVD had to threaten to shoot people to reduce the crush. As the station worker had predicted, there were extra carriages on the train, and the length of the train meant that the end carriages stopped some distance from the station, nearer to Eugenia and her friends. They clambered aboard and found places near the air vents, before the people on the station arrived and started fighting for places.

Once assured of a place on board, the refugees relaxed, and when Eugenia started singing, they joined in loudly. As the train pulled out of the station, she peered through the grille. Sabina was sitting alone on the station waiting forlornly for news of her sister, who was trapped in the quarantined train. She felt sorrow for the girl, but the draw of freedom was too strong for her to dwell on it. Perhaps things would turn out well for Sabina in the end.

As they travelled south, they picked up more Polish ex-prisoners, who somehow squeezed into tiny corners. Many looked desperately ill and were thin and weak, hardly able to climb onto the train without help. Children in particular were skeleton-like with rags for clothes. As she looked at the children in the truck, Eugenia thought of Halina and Ola and she spent days worrying about them. What if they looked like these children? Who would help them and look after them? The euphoria she had felt until then faded and was replaced with fear for her children. She brought out the photographs from her case. She would start asking everyone she saw if they knew her daughters and she would show her photographs to all who would look.

As they waited at yet another station, several days journey from Tashkent, a Polish consul official came to speak to them. 'There is an army division near Dzhalal-Abad and anyone who is fit can volunteer. We are also arranging help for the many orphans and other refugees. Once you get to Tashkent, an aid worker will direct you to the most suitable destination for you. You are among the first of the refugees to arrive.'

Eugenia became more and more hopeful with every mile travelled. Surely someone would have heard of Halina? Perhaps there might even be soldiers who knew Kazimierz. This was what had kept her fighting through her difficulties: the chance that she might find her family again. She felt an unfamiliar emotion. She laughed. It was happiness. She had forgotten what it was to be happy.

Thirty Three

Halina, September 1941, Barnaul Labour Camp

Despite the mud, the exhausting work and the lack of food, Halina was determined to remain optimistic and try to improve her situation. 'Most of the people here when we arrived seemed to have given up,' she remarked to Anita as they stood at the stove heating water one evening, 'we will not.'

Mornings and evenings she washed and tried to get herself as clean as possible, days were spent working as hard and as enthusiastically as possible with the aim of becoming a Stakhanoviet worker and receiving better treatment. Cleaning herself and her clothes was made much more difficult by the fact that she was knee deep in clay each day, but she did not want to end up like the other women in the camp, who seemed resigned to remaining dirty.

The overcrowding in the barracks made the task even more difficult. There was nowhere warm to dry clothes, and each evening the room was lined with damp mildewed clothes hung up to dry. Many had been soaked by working in rain, by perspiration or by attempts at washing. As the evenings became colder, the air became saturated with moisture from the clothes and only those near the stoves had any chance of drying.

The doors were locked at night, which meant buckets had to be used, as the latrines were outside. The buckets that Halina had been forced to use in prison had barely been sufficient for the twenty or thirty she shared a cell with - in the barracks there were over a hundred people and too few buckets. After listening to some of the women, she gathered that the inmates cleaned the barracks at regular intervals, but overcrowding was such that this was impossible. Every spare inch of floor space was occupied. The inability to clean the barracks was another reason that the group from Starodub was resented.

Each night as she lay down in her tiny space, still wearing her coat and using her case for a pillow, Halina tried hard to escape to her dreams of Poland and her family, dreams that had helped her through in the past. But it was so difficult. Noises from the other prisoners, the biting and itching of insects and worst of all, the smell, kept bringing her back to the present. The smell of a hundred unwashed bodies, the smell of damp, mouldy clothes, the smell of odours produced by digestive systems in turmoil, the smell of the toilet buckets. She would have to try to ignore it all. She got used to the stink of Homel prison. She could do it here. She had no choice.

Each day she worked as hard as she could, spurred on by the dream of better conditions, but despite her hard work and diligence at the tasks, she was not given any better food. A portion of dark bread in the morning, some soup in the afternoon and occasionally in the evening was the usual fare, and that did not change however hard she worked. She tried to talk to the Polish women in her barracks about it, but they just shrugged and turned away.

Eventually she found a woman from one of the other barracks who had not experienced the treatment of the Starodub Soviet gang. 'There are no Stakhanoviet here,' she said dully, 'There may have been at one time, but everyone became so weak they stopped trying and no one bothers any more. Even if someone does work harder, the guards do not care. Besides,' she added, 'it would put everyone else under pressure.'

Halina gradually realised that the situation would not improve. She had become weaker and thinner and had diminishing energy left for the constant washing and boiling to keep her clothes clean. The truth had been there from the start, but was something else she had pushed to the back of her mind, until at last she was forced to accept it. She admitted to Stasia one evening, that she found it increasingly difficult to continue the routine. In addition, she was always hungry. 'I think we will have to accept that nothing can improve here,' she said, 'but I am not prepared to carry on like Lola and her gang.'

She lay on the bunk trying to conserve the little energy she had. She kept her school coat on at all times, partly because it was so cold, and partly because she was afraid that it might be stolen. Lola's gang spent much of their free time stealing from the other women in the barracks, and she was determined to keep what she had. She had seen Lola eyeing her coat enviously on more than one occasion. A Soviet girl had taken her precious school uniform. They were not going to get her coat.

'Have you noticed that Lola leaves the barracks some evenings and is away for some time?' Lucia, as observant as ever, spoke to Halina one evening. 'Not only that. Although Lola appears to work as hard as the rest of us, she does not seem to have lost as much weight. I reckon she is getting extra food.'

Halina had noticed that Lola and some of her Soviet gang had quiet conversations with the guards who walked with the group, but had thought nothing of it until then.

'For services rendered,' Halina added. Of course, that was exactly what she would expect Lola to do.

That night she watched Lola and sure enough, she left the barracks when most people had gone to sleep. The door to the barracks was usually locked at night, so that meant Lola must have asked one of the guards to leave it unlocked. She got up and followed her into the night. Lola went round the side of the barracks as if going to the latrines, but once she was behind the building she stopped. A few minutes later, one of the guards came towards her and pushed her against the wall. 'Food first,' Lola said, pushing him away. The guard took a bag out of his tunic and gave it to her. She spent several minutes ravenously gorging the contents then threw the bag on the ground.

While Lola and the guard wrestled against the barracks wall, a gust of wind blew the bag close to Halina. She stretched out her arm and just managed to pull it towards her. She jumped up and ran back inside. Whatever happened, Lola must not see her. Who knows what she would do to keep her activities secret.

Once safely back in the barracks, and underneath the clothing that counted as blankets, she put her hand inside the bag. In the corner were two small crusts of bread, which had been soaked with the juice of something fishy. She savoured the tiny crusts as if they were a banquet, then turned the bag inside out and licked the surface, picking off flakes of bread here and there. Not enough to come anywhere near satisfying her hunger, but she would be able to taste the flavour of fresh bread and fish throughout the night. That was worth risking Lola's wrath.

The next day was a free day, one of the few days that they did not have to work. As Halina lay on the floor shivering, she thought over the events of the night before. Lola and her group had reverted to their status as true criminals. In Starodub they had been controlled by the order in the camp, here they were in charge of the environment in the barracks, while appearing to be compliant in the presence of authority. They were in their element. Brought up on the streets of large towns, they were prepared to do whatever was necessary to survive. They bullied the other prisoners, and stole whatever they could, even to the extent of taking food from the weak and ill if the opportunity arose. They sold themselves for food to whichever of the guards was willing to take the risk of being discovered. Perhaps they might even be prepared to kill if they thought they could get away with it.

However, was she much better? She had been polite and well brought up. She had attended Mass regularly, she knew right from wrong, and yet she was prepared to risk punishment just to lick crumbs from a paper bag. She rushed to the front of the food queue and ignored the fact that those at the end of the queue got no food. She lay in filth covered in lice. All this time the Soviets had been trying to change her to follow their ideals. They had not done that, but look at her now. They had succeeded in degrading her after all.

Halina sat up suddenly as a thought came to her. She took her little tinder box out of her case. Perhaps she could polish it up and sell it for food. However, just as suddenly the thought vanished. It was Papa's. She could not sink to that level. She would not. If she did, they would have won. She wiped away some tears and felt for the dirty smelly ball that was once her mother's shawl. 'Mama, oh Mama, I wish you were here,' she whispered, over and over again until sleep claimed her.

As September gradually ebbed, the spectre of a Siberian winter grew ever closer. Snow lay on the ground and each morning was a little deeper, so that the walk to and from the fields soaked Halina's boots through. The floor of the barracks became wet as well as muddy, and each night she had to fight to get her boots near to the stove to dry them out before the next day.

Halina lay on her bed and wrapped her arms across her chest. She must try to keep warm. Almost October and it was freezing everywhere. She had thought that with all the bodies in the barracks it would be warmer, but it was cold and damp. She looked at Lucia lying just a few inches from her. Poor Lucia, she had found it very difficult the last few weeks. She was asleep, but there were two white tracks where tears had carved a path through the mud on her face. She reached over and picked off an errant louse wandering along the tracks. Funny how she enjoyed squashing them now. It was one small way she could exert a little control. So unlike the first time she had found lice in Homel prison.

A spasm gripped her inside. So many aches and pains. Was it the memories of Mama that had caused the pain? More likely hunger or perhaps the diarrhoea that had emerged in the last few days. The spasm past. Just hunger then.

She closed her eyes but could not sleep. It was so cold and she was so hungry. She had only been at the camp two months, but already she was fading away. How had those other women lasted a year? She recalled something one of the other women had said. The food had been better before the Germans invaded, but the main reason was they had brought food with them and had received food parcels until the Germans declared war on the Soviets. Whatever the reason, they were all in the same state now. How much longer could she last? She still had just enough energy to get up and walk to the brickfields. Only just. Once winter really took hold, she would not manage it. Her spirit had kept her going and would for a while. But not for much longer. She could not counteract the effect of lack of food. She closed her eyes. If she could sleep, she just might dream of Mama, of Poland. She finally drifted off to oblivion.

A troupe of bed bugs marched towards her. Their banquet was about to begin.

Thirty Four

Halina, October 1941, Barnaul District

One morning in late September, the day started differently. Instead of being escorted to their workplace, the camp was told to wait after roll call. The commandant stood on a small stage with several NKVD men on either side. 'Our great leader Stalin has made an agreement with the Polish government in London,' he announced, 'There is an amnesty and all Polish internees are to be released.'

He carried on talking about a Polish army being formed in Uzbekistan, but Halina hardly heard him. She looked at her companions to confirm that what she had heard was true. Freedom! It was a miracle.

One of the Soviet girls standing next to Halina turned to her, 'You lucky Poles,' she said, 'you can go, but we must stay here and die.'

It was hard to take in the news, and it was evening before the implications sank in. Halina stood inside the barracks, now packed with everyone back from work. Adrenaline surged through her body and her heart started beating so quickly she felt light-headed. Was Stasia talking to her? Something about making a real effort to get clean. She would have the energy for that now. It had really happened. The miracle that she had prayed for every night had happened. She felt a sudden jolt. What if it was a dream? She looked around. The Polish inmates in the barracks were taunting Lola and her gang and were even taking back some of the items stolen from them. She sighed with relief. She was not dreaming.

She chewed on her bread. The bread had improved dramatically and even the soup was drinkable now. Commandant Korallov must have had the supplies all along. In a few days, she would have her photograph taken for the necessary documents and then....she hugged herself gleefully...then they would be free. Only a few days ago, she had been worn out and miserable, now she could hardly contain her excitement. Life was something to look forward to again. She picked up her filthy clothes. Those lice had better watch out.

The next few days passed in a daze. They had photographs taken and paperwork was issued, but Halina could hardly bear to look at her photograph. She was so thin she looked like a skeleton. She looked dreadful. She had seen the others becoming thin and wasted, but somehow thought she would look different. She looked just as bad as they did. She put it in her pocket. At least the atmosphere in the barracks had changed dramatically. The Soviet girls no longer held sway, and the Polish inmates treated them with the contempt they had feared showing before.

The day of their departure finally came. The Poles were gathered together and to their surprise and amazement, they were issued with padded jackets, boots, some violet underwear and forty roubles each. Now that they were free, they regained hope, and their sense of humour.

'Why on earth is the underwear violet!' Anita laughed.

'Perhaps it has been specially disinfected to keep lice out,' said Stasia.

'Imagine the Soviets giving us these clothes,' exclaimed Lucia.

'I very much doubt they did,' Irena said, 'probably the Polish government paid for it all.'

An even bigger surprise was that they were allowed a steam bath with plentiful soap, water and disinfectant. One of the camp inmates, communicative now that freedom beckoned, told Halina that when they first came to the camp in 1940 they used the steam bath once a month. The worst of their clothes were thrown away and the rest disinfected. The group gathered up their belongings and walked through the gates for the last time. They walked along the path, which led them past the brick making area. Everyone was singing Polish songs loudly and cheerfully. Only a few days ago life had seemed hopeless, death a certainty - now they had new hope, new life. Halina felt so happy inside that it was almost painful. Stasia even had the energy to dance around as if at a ball.

'Look, the Soviet girls are making bricks on their own,' she cried as a twirl brought her close to the edge of the field. The Soviet girls turned in their direction, their faces full of envy and misery. Halina looked across at the field. They had won the final round. The Polish girls had won.

As they walked along the track, they discussed their next move.

'We have been told there will be work in the factories if we want it,' Irena said, 'but I am not sure I do. I would rather try and find a train to take me away from here.'

'But we don't know where to go,' Anita replied. 'Perhaps we should rest for a bit and try and find out a route. '

Halina felt rather as if she had been floating above the ground for the last week, hovering above the sticky grey earth, not affected by cold or discomfort. Now she was on the road to freedom, her feet touched the ground again.

'We need to find somewhere to stay out of the cold,' she suggested to her friends.

'With a stove,' added Lucia.

'And food,' said Stasia.

They walked along the road, stepping round the puddles and trying to avoid the mud - not an easy task. In the end, they just ploughed through everything intent on their mission. They separated into smaller groups, as they decided that would make it easier to find somewhere to stay. Halina with Stasia and Lucia, walked away from the camp towards the town of Barnaul, anxious to put some distance between them and their former prison. In the distance, they could see narrow plumes of smoke rising up, hardly moving in the still air. On either side of the road were fields, with small wooden houses here and there. After walking for some time, they passed an overgrown field with a small wooden cottage in one corner.

'No one seems to be doing anything with that field,' said Stasia, 'Looks like there is no one around.'

They made their way towards the cottage. It was small and square with no windows and looked rather like a barn except that there was a small chimney coming out of the roof. Halina walked up to the door that hung slightly open and peered inside. Inside, the cottage was very dark, with light coming only from the open door. The floor was of hard packed earth and rather uneven, but it appeared dry. She stumbled across the room in the dim light and just avoided walking into a large stone object. 'It's a stove,' she said, hardly believing her luck. 'There is no one around, the cottage must have been abandoned, but there is a stove.'

The others came in excitedly.

'There are bits of wood and sticks next to the stove,' said Stasia, 'so at least we will be warm.'

'There's a sledge in the corner,' exclaimed Lucia, 'and it is in good condition.'

Halina looked around, and as her eyes became accustomed to the gloom, she made out a rough table, chairs and even a simple wooden bed in the corner. The furniture was rotted through, as she found out when she sat on the bed, but she decided it would make good firewood. Next to the stove there were some cups and wooden plates, several battered metal pots and a wooden tub. Hanging on the wall was an old oil lamp, but there was no oil to be found.

Lucia was busy raking through the stove. 'The chimney looks fine,' she said and she piled sticks and wood carefully in the bottom of the stove. 'How are we going to light it?' asked Stasia, as practical as ever.

For a moment, Halina thought of her tinderbox and the flint inside and almost volunteered to use it. Edmund would approve. However, it was an important part of her memories. She did not want it to become merely a tool. Then she had another idea. She went to the door and looked back at a house they had passed before coming to the cottage. 'That house over there has smoke coming from its chimney, so there must be someone there,' she announced, 'We could try and exchange something for food and at the same time perhaps they will give us some embers to light the fire. That way we can preserve our few matches.'

They debated what they could afford to sell and decided on a pair of old boots. The new boots they had been given at the labour camp had replaced their old muddy boots, which with a bit of a clean, would look reasonable. Even in their worn state, they were much better than any they had seen worn by the Russians they had encountered. Halina picked up one of the metal pots near the stove and made her way to the nearby house.

She banged on the door, which was opened by a woman wearing worn ragged clothing topped by a headscarf. For once, Halina was glad she had learned Russian in Starodub.

'Hello. Does anyone live in that cottage over there,' she said pointing to her new home.

'They have gone,' said the house owner.

'We have come from the labour camp,' Halina continued, 'and hoped we could stay in the cottage, but we need to light the fire. Can you spare some embers? Also we have some boots we would like to exchange for some food, if you have it.'

The old woman looked at her a little longer. 'You have been released from the labour camp,' she said, looking incredulous, '..Oh, you must be Poles.'

She looked at the boots and Halina was glad that she had guessed correctly. The woman had no proper shoes on her feet, which were wrapped in rags. Her face lit up when she saw them, worn as they were. She took the pot, turned back into the house and returned a few minutes later with a small cabbage, some bread and the pot, full of red embers.

'There is a stream behind the cottage, but it will freeze up soon. Then you must go to the pump,' she said and shut the door firmly.

Halina went back to the cottage, and carefully tipped the embers into the centre of Lucia's careful edifice. They took turn in blowing the glowing wood, and the sticks soon took light. After a few more minutes, the fire was burning brightly. Halina told the others what the old woman had said about water and Stasia took the now empty and newly sterilised pot outside, returning with water.

'And look what else I have,' she said, placing the pot on the rapidly warming surface of the stove. She held up two enormous potatoes. 'They are not in a very good state, but they look edible.'

That night they sat round the stove sitting on pieces of wood to keep them from the cold floor. The chairs had also proved to be broken and crumbled as they sat on them, but they provided some planks of wood. Freshly boiled underwear was steaming in a corner. Earlier that evening, they had the luxury of a thorough wash in hot water using the wooden tub. It had meant several trips out to get water from the stream, but that they hardly noticed. Halina's small and precious piece of soap had been almost used up, but finally, she actually felt clean. Even the violet, scratchy underwear given at the camp seemed luxurious, as it was clean, unstained and new.

'If only the tub was bigger we could have a real bath,' said Lucia, wistfully.

As they waited for the food to cook on the stove, they sat in the faint light of the open door, carefully combing each other's hair looking for any remaining signs of parasites. It was such a relief to be away from the infested environment of the labour camp, Halina was able to think about the subject of parasites with hope, for the first time. They would have to continue the ritual each night for several weeks to ensure they were truly free of lice, but there was the real chance that they would be rid of them. It was hard to believe.

She looked at the feast newly served, her mouth watering - thick soup made from potatoes and cabbage, bread and even a dessert made from a few, battered, red berries Lucia had found growing under some trees. She could hardly remember what potatoes tasted like. She would have to eat slowly, savour each mouthful and make it last. It was a heady combination- food, heat and cleanliness - all things at one time she would barely have considered. Now she knew better. When you have had nothing, even the most basic of necessities seem like priceless luxuries.

That night, before dropping off to sleep, Halina revelled in the truly intoxicating feeling of relief that she was once again free. Only a few days ago, life had seemed intolerable, yet something to cling onto with every nerve straining. Only a few days ago, it had seemed unlikely that she would live for much longer, that the cold of winter would creep in like a thief in the night stealing the very last of her strength. A terrible, heavy feeling of melancholy had pressed down on her day after day so that she could barely raise her mind, let alone her body, above it. Now the weights had lifted, and she understood the true meaning of the phrase 'light hearted'.

She slept soundly that night despite the hard uncomfortable ground. The cottage was very dark with only a little light entering under the door, but the only noise was the gentle rustle of the burning wood. There were no cries of the sick, no sound of tears of despair, no sighing of souls lost. Best of all, there was no bite of insects.

Thirty Five

Halina, October 1941, Barnaul District

Halina woke in the early morning and put more wood on the fire as it threatened to fade. The heat from the stove had dried the clothes washed the night before, and she enjoyed the unaccustomed luxury of putting on clean underwear for the second day in a row. Stasia and Lucia stirred.

'Do you realise,' said Stasia, 'that there are no bedbugs here? Can you believe it? That was first night for months that I have not been on the menu of some wretched parasite.'

'What's for breakfast?' asked Lucia.

'There is bread toasted over wood, with hot water and cabbage tea,' Halina replied, 'provided I can find something to spear the bread.' She searched around and found a rather battered-looking fork. 'The fire will sterilise it,' she added, waving the fork in the air.

For the second time in twenty-four hours, Halina had something approaching a meal, enjoyed in warmth and what now seemed like comfort. However, the euphoria started to fade a little as she used the last of the bread and realised they had nothing left to eat.

'We really must decide what to do now,' said Stasia.

Halina sat crunching her toast and drinking the hot water and cabbage tea, sitting as close to the stove as she dare, as they discussed their options. 'I know they said at the camp that there was to be a Polish army formed, but they did not tell us where.'

'How can we travel thousands of miles without really knowing where we are going,' asked Lucia, 'We do not know if there are Soviets or Germans in Poland, even if we knew how to get there.'

'We have hardly any money, no food and we are all still very weak from the labour camp, and Halina, you said only a few days ago that you were feeling ill. I think we should stay here for a bit, get a job in the factory and wait for some news,' added Stasia.

Halina wanted so much to get on a train and leave the terrible place. She longed for Poland and her family so much it felt truly painful to think of putting that off. However, now that she had fewer worries, she had become more aware that the headaches and stomach pains she had endured for several weeks were not due to cold or hunger. She knew Stasia was right. After all, she might be fine in a few more weeks. First, they must collect more wood and water. She took the bucket to the stream to get water and noticed that it was beginning to freeze. It would not be long before it became solid ice. Stasia gathered some wood from round about, but Halina could see that there was very little suitable wood left in the vicinity, which made her a little nervous. Keeping warm was the first priority in a Russian winter. Stasia piled as much wood on the fire as she could, and the trio set off up the dirt road towards Barnaul and the sewing factory.

They walked for about three miles and eventually stood outside a large building. 'Look at those walls. Surely they are made from our bricks,' Halina said, 'but the building looks quite old. I wonder how many years the labour camp has been in the area.'

Once inside, they were directed to an office where a woman with short iron-grey hair sat looking at some documents. 'So, you want to work for the Soviet Union do you,' she said.

Halina gave her the amnesty passes they had received from the camp. 'We used interlock machines in Starodub,' she said.

'Nothing so fancy here,' the woman replied. 'There are machines for sewing and some hand sewing is required - buttons and that sort of thing. We make uniforms here for the gallant men of the glorious Red Army. It is night work, but we do have work for you. There is a canteen here where you can buy food during the day. If you are looking for somewhere to stay, there are places to rent if you look on the notice board,' she added, pointing out a wooden board in the entrance hall.

'I did not realise there would be places to rent,' Halina said, hopeful that she would not have to walk three miles from the cottage to work every day.

'It will not be much fun walking here in the dark, so we need somewhere much closer,' Stasia mumbled as she looked through the notices on the board. 'There is one here that looks closer and there is a sort of map with it.' She took it off the notice board and put it in her pocket. 'Don't want anyone else to get it first,' she explained.

Instead of walking straight back to the cottage, Lucia suggested they walk round Barnaul and visit the market. As they passed what looked liked a café, Halina noticed a pile of potatoes at the side of the wooden building. 'What's wrong with them,' asked Lucia, examining the pile closely whilst Halina looked rather nervously around to see if they were being watched. Taking discarded food did not seem like stealing, but she did not want another prison sentence.

'They look fine, Lucia, just take them,' she said, anxious to leave.

They walked further, the potatoes bouncing around in the bag Halina had brought, and found the market. They bought a few vegetables, a small fish, and some bread and then Stasia remembered they would be working nights and persuaded the others to part with a small share of the money for a pair of battered oil lamps.

'All we need is to find some oil,' she said. 'Perhaps we should have thought of that first,' she added later.

The lodgings they had seen for rent were on the way back to their cottage, and only a slight deviation towards the River Ob was required. The street on the note was easy to find, but Halina could not see any houses, just humps in the ground with smoke coming out of the top.

'Dugouts,' exclaimed Lucia, 'Someone at Starodub told me about them. They are underground houses with only the roof above ground. It means they are easier to heat or something.'

Halina knocked at the door under the low roof and a woman came to the door. She showed the woman the advertisement from the factory and she invited them in.

'My husband is sleeping,' she said, 'He works night shift as a stoker at the sewing factory.'

Halina looked around curiously. So this was how the Russians lived. The lodgings were better than their little abandoned cottage, but they were still very primitive. The dugout consisted of one large room dominated by a huge stove, which was twice the size of the one in their abandoned cottage. There were no windows, and the room was lit by several oil lamps. There was a large double bed at one end of the room, and a smaller bed with a young girl in, on the other side. There was a pile of clothes at the back of the stove with a shape underneath them. Halina looked closely. The Russians had some strange habits. The stoker was sleeping on the stove.

The woman went on to explain that she worked on a communal farm and had two other children with her there. She only came home occasionally and would be glad of the extra money from lodgers.

Halina realised she would have to share the large bed with Stasia and Lucia. That would mean they would be warm, especially as there were blankets. However, did she want to share a room with the stoker and his children? There would be no privacy at all.

'My daughter Anya is disabled and spends all her time in bed,' the woman continued, 'and one of my sons also lives here, but he is at school just now. My husband works long hours and eats at the factory, so is not often here. It would be good to know there would be other people here. My neighbours help with Anya and my son.' She told them what she wanted for rent and it seemed quite a small amount when divided among the three of them. 'My husband can buy coal easily,' she added as an incentive, 'He brings it from work. And there is oil available for your lamps.'

Halina looked at the other two and it was obvious that they, like her, had been swayed by the thought of a plentiful supply of oil for the lamps together with coal and hence reliable heat. After all, where else could they go?

'Thank you, we would like to take the room,' she said, while Stasia and Lucia nodded in agreement.

They were shown the coal 'cellar', which was a shallow depression near the door, and Halina examined the 'washroom' which was a small partitioned area at the back of the dugout with a basin, and a bucket she recognised as the toilet. Not much better than in prison and yet the woman was proud of it. Things were very different from Poland. No wonder the Soviet girls bought up everything in sight from the market stalls in Luck.

Halina and her friends agreed to move in that day, and walked back to the cottage, to pick up their belongings. 'It really is very primitive,' she said, 'but it will be warm with that stove, at least. And maybe the woman will bring some food from the farm.'

'I had a look at the bed covers,' said Stasia, 'and they looked reasonably clean. The woman did not look dirty either, so perhaps we have struck it lucky.'

Having so recently come from the filth of the camp, Halina would have accepted almost anywhere to be warm and comfortable. The woman had made it clear that they would be responsible for buying their own food and fetching their water, but they would have free use of the stove and access to coal and oil. The thought of being warm was so pleasant that she was able to ignore the disquiet at the back of her mind. The dugout was little more than a hovel and she had thought the bedding far from clean. Still, compared to Barnaul it was paradise. And she was free.

Thirty Six

Kazimierz when a German prisoner of war.

'..it became clear that he had been captured by the Germans'

Eugenia, October 1941, Soviet Russia

True to the consul's word, Eugenia and the other refugees on the train found an aid worker at Tashkent station. Eugenia spoke to him, saying she was the wife of a Polish army officer, and she was directed with her friends to a train for Dzhalal-Abad where the Polish Fifth Division was encamped. As the train grew nearer to her destination, Eugenia could hardly contain her exhilaration. Everyone in her carriage was in a similar state of mind, and talked and sang loudly. When they finally arrived, there was a great crush to leave the carriage, so Eugenia held back until most had left. She jumped down and with her group of friends walked slowly in the same direction as the other refugees.

It was only a short walk to the camp, and the tents came in view before Eugenia had time to collect her thoughts. 'Janka, look,' she whispered almost afraid to speak in case it was a dream, 'Polish soldiers.'

Janka started shouting and cheering and ran around hugging everyone, and before she knew it Eugenia joined in. She ran up to a soldier and was about to throw her arms round him when she noticed that the smile on his face froze a little. In the heat of the moment, she had forgotten how ragged and dirty she was after a long journey with louse-ridden fellow travellers. 'Sorry,' she said laughing, tears of joy running down her face.

Later that evening she sat on a comfortable mattress in a tent, drinking tea and still thinking of the food she had eaten that day, food that she swore tasted as if it had come from the best restaurant in Poland. She had been washed, disinfected, de-loused and questioned. Her clothes had been burned and she was dressed in woollen underwear and had a uniform at the foot of her bed, together with some clothes she had been given. She was not sure of the source of the women's clothes, and did not inquire too closely. All of hers that remained was the ermine collar. She had managed to find a little yellow dress among the spare items of clothing and had attached the ermine collar to it. The collar had been brushed and repaired, the one little piece of Poland she still had left, and the dress was in pride of place hanging up in the tent. She lay down on the mattress, her heart full.

The next few weeks were full of excitement and disappointment in equal measures. Janka and her daughters had stayed to train as nurses, but Marysia and Teresa had moved to other sites where they were to help with refugee orphans, who were being cared for in a separate camp some miles away. The tearful farewells were softened with promises to meet again when the war was over. Eugenia herself was attached to the education unit, and was soon involved with organising a concert for the soldiers.

At other times, she travelled round the army camp asking everyone if they had seen her daughters, showing the worn photographs each time. Every new arrival was questioned by her, almost before they had eaten their first proper meal, but the answer was always 'No.' She asked about Kazimierz, and although she had no definite news, it became clear that he had been captured by the Germans. The news about Kazimierz had not been good, but somehow she felt much more optimistic about finding Halina. It was a miracle that she herself was alive. Surely one more miracle was not too much to ask?

On the evening of the first concert, she sat outside her tent, preparing poetry for the recital she was to give. She would be thinking of Halina and Ola as she stood on the stage. Would she be able to recite without bursting into tears? So many memories were tied up in those poems. She felt nervous. It was one thing reciting to exhausted women in a labour camp, but tonight the audience would be soldiers. She stroked the collar on her yellow dress. The ermine collar was a little bare in patches, but to her it was precious. It would give her the courage to get up on the stage. She stood up. Tonight she would be Polish again. Reciting Polish poems, wearing Polish ermine and performing to Polish soldiers. She might shed some tears, but they would not be tears of despair as so many had been in the past.

When it came to her turn to perform, her nerves vanished, and as she started to recite, she poured all the pain and longing of the previous two years into the poems. When she had finished the last poem, there was absolute silence. She looked at the audience and saw that many were in tears as they relived their own troubles through her words. Had she been any good? Had they liked her? Suddenly applause started, followed by cheering and shouting. She stood and felt, as much as heard, the love from her audience. The emotion flowed round her and helped to heal some of her wounds.

From that night, she became famous in the camp, and in the ensuing weeks, no concert was complete without Eugenia reciting. Her finest moment arrived when General Sikorski, the Polish leader, was present at one of her recitals. She stood on the stage pouring out her soul, dressed in her yellow dress with the ermine collar, which had become an important part of each performance. At the end, the General, with tears in his eyes, kissed her hand and praised her. Eugenia was overcome. The Polish leader coming to listen to her! She found it difficult to speak and only just managed to stammer replies to his questions about her experiences. However when he told her he had been visiting several army camps, she managed to say, 'Have you seen my daughter Halina?'

Halina, December 1941, Barnaul District

Halina wrapped herself in as many layers of clothing as she could and wound her scarf round her head. With the two small and battered lanterns they had bought in the market plus the old one from the cottage, there was a lamp for her as well as Stasia and Lucia. She had filled her lamp earlier using the precious store of oil in the dugout. Thank goodness Stasia had the foresight to ensure each of them had a lamp. With great care, she lit the wick using a stick from the fire. She did not want to use her small store of matches if she could avoid it. The lamp flickered and finally glowed, and she ventured into the night.

When she had been told that only night work was available at the factory, it had not seemed too bad. At least she would have the few hours of daylight to enjoy, she had reasoned. Not that it would have made much difference what she thought - that was the only work available and she had no choice but to take it. It was such a disappointment that the three of them started work at different times. She was working in a different part of the factory and on a slightly different shift from Stasia and Lucia. She had to travel to and from work on her own and in the dark.

The working conditions in the factory were another disappointment. She had to work long hours in cold, dusty, cramped, noisy conditions, and for very little pay. There was enough for rent and basic food, but little for clothing or for good quality food. She closed the dugout door behind her. She had been so sure things would turn out well after being freed from the camp, but her health had not improved.

It was so unfair. Stasia and Lucia had gradually put on weight and had become stronger, but the fevers and headaches that she had suffered for the last few weeks in the labour camp, had not abated. Now after two months of freedom, she had put on little weight and still felt tired and weak all the time. Surely she would win the battle soon?

For so long it seemed she had fought. Her first fights had been with her father, starting when she was fourteen. To think at times she had imagined him as the enemy! How foolish and childish she had been. The real enemy of course was the Soviets, and there she had gained strength from her victories, however small. Now the enemy was her own body and it thwarted her at every turn. If only her fever would go. It sucked out what little strength she had, so that the only battle she could win was in her head. She had to ignore her weakening body and force herself onwards. So far, she was the victor, but for how long could the fight continue?

It was bitterly cold outside. Just as well, there was no thermometer around - at least she could imagine it was only just below freezing, although it was probably closer to twenty degrees below. The factory was about twenty minutes walk from the dugout, and in daylight she had decided it was about the same distance she had walked to school in Kamionka and easily manageable. However a twenty-minute walk in daylight with her friends was a very different matter at night on her own, and each night she took the path, the journey seemed longer than the one before.

December was well established and the cold of the Russian winter touched everything with fingers of steel. The ground was rough in places with holes and ruts that were obvious in daylight, but which could not be seen in the dim lantern light. In other places, the icy surface was glass smooth and slippery, and she slipped, slithered, and tripped over the ruts. She fell several times, bruising her elbow and then landed with a stunning crash on her bottom. She stood up, shaken and aching. She would have to travel very slowly and carefully if she was to arrive without any further mishaps.

Perhaps if she thought of something pleasant it would make the journey easier. She thought back to a memorable time when, aged fourteen, she had walked back from school with her mother, her mother's friend Anita and Anita's son Stefan. It was the first time she had met Stefan. He had just returned from finishing his first year at Lwow University where he was studying mathematics. She fell in love at once and probably by the time she got home, he had realised it. She blushed. It was so long ago now. Why was she blushing after so long?

If she could manage to conjure up the memory of that day, it might distract her from the darkness of the night. It had been an afternoon in June. The sun had been shining and in the sheltered streets, the air had been hot. A little of the warmth of that day filtered through her imagination and she almost started to feel the sun. If she concentrated hard, she might even be able to imagine that her mother and Anita were walking behind and that she was trying to keep up with Stefan's long strides. Yes, she could almost hear him now. He was talking about the university and his professors and the good time he was having there. She could even see his face in front of her - his eyes shining with the pleasure of his tales. The journey back from school had been so short then, she had prayed for the time to stretch so that she could bask for longer in his brilliance. Now, the journey seemed so long.

She slipped once more and just managed to stop falling, the exertion dragging her back to the ice-cold reality of the Russian winter. A few flakes of snow started to fall and a wind sprang up, its icy fingers tugged at her clothing seeking a way in to torment her. She was bent almost double peering closely at the road, one freezing hand holding the lantern, the other pulling her scarf tightly round her face. Would she ever arrive?

Suddenly, the lights of Barnaul town appeared through the gloom. Now she could extinguish the flame from the lamp and preserve precious fuel. No longer would ruts and holes torment her as the road was smoother here, being in the town. She jumped as a half-formed shape in an alleyway came towards her. It was just the shadow of a tree. She must stop imagining things that were not there. That was the problem with an overdeveloped imagination, although it was useful when she wanted to take her mind off her surroundings. The austere grey walls of the factory loomed in front of her and she sighed with relief. She had arrived. If only her hand would stop shaking. She must be careful. It would be a disaster if she dropped the lamp.

As the factory drew nearer, she could see other workers arriving, dressed in layers of clothing with scarves tightly pulled around their faces. No one smiled. No one spoke. At least she was no longer alone with her nightmares. She entered the factory and made her way to the huge sewing hall. There were rows and rows of tables with sewing machines, their motors controlled by foot pedals. In one section, groups of women sat round a table, sewing on buttons. The air was dusty and had a strong chemical smell from the dyes used on the cloth. Worst of all was the noise. There were dozens of machines there, all contributing to the noise level.

She hated the noise. The electric motors whined, the needles tapped, and the sounds echoing from the high ceilings reverberated round, doubling the noise and distorting it, until it sounded like an orchestra from hell. The girls on the machines sang songs most of the night, but the tunes only sounded sweet to the singer - to her the noise was like a devil's choir. The hall was very cold and dimly lit, but above each of the machines was a bright white light. Was she imagining it, or did the light above the machine seemed sharper and whiter than usual? Each time she looked at the material before her, the light drove like a knife into her head, sending sharp splinters of pain into the constant background throbbing. She was very tired, but she had to keep her eyes open. She needed the work. She needed the money. She had to get away from Russia.

The shifts were eleven hours long with only two short breaks. At the first break, she made her way to the washroom, her legs stiff with the tension of working the foot pedal. She stood at the washbasin, trying to straighten her back, which seemed permanently fixed in its crouched position. She leaned her head against the cold concrete wall behind the basin and splashed water in her face. She had to bring some life back into her sleepy eyes. She was hungry and picked up her bread but the grey doughy centre was tasteless. The usual hot water was available for drinking and she peeled the crust off the bread and dropped it, piece by piece into the water. Why did it look so awful? She took a mouthful and felt sick. What was wrong with her? Normally she could convince herself it was a tasty soup. But not tonight.

Back at her seat in the factory, she closed her eyes and drifted off to sleep, dreaming of clear running water and spring flowers. She imagined she was once more in the flower meadow she had stopped at on her journey to Barnaul. She reached out her hand to pick a flower and heard a bird singing nearby. The singing became louder, but the flower moved further away. She woke with a start. It was not a bird singing, but the bell to signal the end of break.

When at last the long shift was over, she barely had the strength to wrap herself in her layers and walk out of the gates. She still had that awful journey back to the dugout. Although it was seven in the morning, it was pitch black. It was snowing and a cold sharp wind drove the snow into her face, stinging and slicing its way into every crevice. As she stumbled along the street, she noticed two drunks ahead, singing loudly and weaving their way from side to side as they approached her. She had to avoid them. She did not have the energy to deal with them.

She moved into the field at the side of the road. There was little light there, and she fell up to her waist in a snowdrift. It was cold, but she would just have to wait until they passed. The snow was deep and soft and it was a struggle to extract herself. Why bother? It would be so easy to stay there and sleep. But she might never wake up. She did not want to stay out in the cold any longer, not when there was heat waiting in the dugout. She struggled out, and walked unsteadily for the last half mile, too tired to brush the snow from her coat. As the dugout came into view, she made a decision. She could not face that journey again. She was ill. She just could not go to work until she felt better.

Thirty Seven

Halina, December 1941, Barnaul District

Inside the dugout, Stasia and Lucia were already home. They had started their shifts an hour before Halina and thus finished earlier. The stoker was not due to arrive for several hours more, so they had the dugout to themselves, except for Anja, who as usual was lying in her small bed in the corner. Soup was heating on the stove. Halina poured some out and sat on a stool sipping it and revelling in the smell and taste. Her hands were so cold, she could hardly hold the cup, but gradually she began to thaw out.

'I won't be able to go to work tomorrow,' she said, 'I just don't feel well enough.'

Stasia started to say something, but a look from Lucia stopped her. 'Will you be able to fetch water from the pump, Halina?'

Halina could tell that the news had not pleased Stasia. She had not imagined it then. She had noticed recently that Stasia was becoming impatient with the fact that her health had not improved. She had a sinking feeling in her chest. She did not want to have to venture out again with the sledge and drag the water back to the dugout, but she did not want to let her friends down. 'I will get it when I have had a rest and when the sun is up,' she replied. Around noon, she managed to find the energy to go out again and fetch water from the pump. She came back into the dugout and began to feel frightened. She barely had the strength to lift herself into bed.

She slept throughout the afternoon and the next night. When finally she woke up, the stoker was snoring in his makeshift bed at the back of the stove. His son was at school, Anja was with a neighbour, and Lucia and Stasia were fast asleep after a long night's work. She felt more than a little lonely. The light from the fire flickered on the dark walls of the dugout casting a dancing shadow that reminded her of shadow puppets.

She began to think of the first time her father had set up a shadow puppet theatre for her when she was very small. He had rigged up a sheet and a lantern and told her to sit down. She remembered sitting looking at the sheet wondering what was going to happen, when suddenly it came to life with rabbits and dragons and other animals all woven together with a story that she did not really understand, but loved all the same. She had been a little frightened and needed reassured that there really were no dragons behind the sheet. She got out of bed and moved her hand to cast a shadow on the wall. But it was no fun on her own.

A tear started to roll down her face as she thought of home and family. It was depressing sitting in the half darkness, but there was no point in moping. She should go outside. Mama had always said that fresh air would do her good. She pulled her coat on, wrapped her scarf round her head and face and pushed her feet into her boots. Well, the air in Russia was nothing if not fresh.

The sun was out and the reflection from the snow hurt her eyes. Blinking hard, she turned and looked around her. Fresh snow had fallen in the night and everything was clothed in a blanket of silence. There was no wind, no life, and no sound. Only snow. The snow although fresh, already had a firm crust on it. As she walked, her feet crunched on the surface, which resisted at first, then finally gave an ill-tempered grunt and sank a few inches.

She had intended going straight to the factory canteen, then remembered that she had heard there was a bathhouse nearby. She had tried hard to keep clean using the basic facilities in the dugout, but always felt dirty. The luxury of a thorough wash in warm surroundings was tempting. Perhaps it would make her feel better. At least there would be some people around.

The bathhouse was close to the factory and she bought her ticket at the door of the steamy building to wait her turn in the queue. She entered the women's area and was handed a small piece of soap and a towel and directed towards a basin that had just been filled with hot water. The room was very hot and steamy. She washed and lathered thoroughly, feeling cleaner than she had in a while. After rubbing herself with the rough towel, she did in fact feel better and her spirits lifted a little. The canteen was a short distance away and she walked there eagerly, wanting to retain the newly acquired heat as long as possible.

She reached the canteen door and ventured inside. She felt hungry but could not afford more than soup and bread. At least the soup was quite thick. She paid for it and sat down at a table. There were a few people around, and the mere presence of human bodies would help to ease the ache of loneliness in her chest.

After her food, she sat enjoying the comparative warmth of the canteen. It was time she faced up to the fact that she really was ill. She had expected to feel much better after leaving the camp and having access to better food, but the improvement had only been temporary. If she did not get better soon, she would never be able to leave Russia. She had felt weak and sick many times before in prison and the labour camp, but that was always due to lack of food.

This new feeling was different. She had to accept that she was getting weaker. Nothing she ate seemed to stay long enough to nourish her, and any exertion left her feeling completely exhausted. Therefore, she had to do something positive. She looked at the information posters on the canteen wall, and saw one describing a clinic nearby. What a bit of luck. Now things would get better.

The clinic was little more than a room at the end of an entrance hall. After sitting for two hours in the hall, surrounded by men, women and children coughing, sneezing or bleeding, she almost wished she had not come, but eventually her name was called. She was taken to see someone she assumed was a doctor. He seemed very old - tall and thin with grey hair cut short but surprisingly thick. Untidy grey eyebrows sprouted above dark eyes, and he had square stolid features.

He took her temperature and pulse and examined her with a stethoscope. 'Very thin,' he muttered. 'Do you have enough food?'

'Yes, but I have diarrhoea,' Halina ventured, 'and I do not seem to be getting better.'

He poked and prodded a few minutes longer and asked more questions.

'How long has this weakness lasted?'

'About six weeks'

'Have you had a fever for long?'

'For several weeks I have felt cold and hot but not all the time.'

'Do the symptoms change from day to day?'

'Some days I shiver and cannot stop it. Other days I feel hot, some days neither. But I have been feeling weaker each day.'

The doctor put away his stethoscope. 'We can do nothing. You have a high fever and must go to hospital.' With that, he wrote a brief note and told her to leave. When Halina said she did not know where the hospital was, he wrote down some directions, and pointed to the door. Not once had he looked her in the eye. But at least she was making progress.

Thirty Eight

Halina, December 1941, Barnaul District

On her return from the clinic, Halina saw a stall owner with some milk and her mouth salivated at the thought. It was a positive sign that things were improving – she had not had milk for over a year. With the help of her last few roubles, she managed to persuade the market stall owner to sell her a little. After all, Christmas was a few days away and she deserved a treat. On returning to the dugout, she poured the precious cargo into a pan, placed it on the stove and sat on a stool, pulling her scarf tightly round her. The warmth from the fire made her feel a little better and she watched entranced as the white liquid started to heat slowly and form a wrinkled skin on the surface. When she judged it hot enough she took the pan off the heat and moved it towards a piece of bread she had cut. Now to imagine that the milk skin was butter. Best to take her time and savour the process. Who knows when she would find milk again.

She took a small knife, gingerly lifted the milk skin out of the pan and laid it on the bread. She patted it with the flat of the knife and sat back to admire her creation. Yes! If she half closed her eyes, it really did look like butter. Memories of butter thickly spread on fresh crusty loaves invaded her thoughts, and almost in a daze, she lifted the bread to her mouth. Now if she closed her eyes and concentrated it would taste like butter. Thick creamy butter. Delicious! Each mouthful was a pleasure that washed over her whole body. She took sips of milk, allowing the sweet fragrant liquid to flush the last few crumbs of bread from hiding places in the crevices of her mouth. She opened her eyes again. There was no bread or milk left. A few moments pleasure and then it was gone. Perhaps if she closed her eyes again……..yes, she could taste it all over again. She just had to shake out her memories. Memories of the taste would keep her company for some time.

Lucia and Stasia stirred and woke up and the spell was broken. She must tell Stasia and Lucia that she had to go to hospital. They were bound to be pleased that she was getting help for her illness, but she should wait until they had dressed and were sitting next to her with their breakfast of toasted bread and tea. Then she could give them the good news.

'I went to a clinic today and they said I could go to hospital,' she said, smiling at her friends. The response she got was not what she had expected.

Stasia put down her cup and snorted, 'Hospital! What on earth will we do when you are in hospital? You don't earn any money and loaf about all day, but at least you fetched the water.'

'But I am ill,' Halina started to say.

'You are always saying you are ill, Halina! You are so selfish.' Stasia lifted up her cup again. 'We are tired enough when work is over and now we will have to go out in the snow and drag that wretched sledge to get water.'

Halina glared at Stasia in fury, 'How dare you say I am selfish! I am not selfish! Do you think I want to be ill? Does it not occur to you how much I want to get better and go away from this dreadful country? I had hoped that by going to hospital and being cured, I would help everyone, but all you can think of is yourself. You are the selfish one!' With that, she pulled on her outside clothes and stormed out of the dugout into the late afternoon light.

She walked towards the river, her fists clenched, feeling light headed after her outburst. They had gone through so much together, the three of them, and had always supported each other. Whenever Stasia or Lucia had been unhappy, she had tried to comfort them, whenever there were problems they had discussed them and solved them, but now they had abandoned her. How could they! As she stood on the riverbank, her anger dissipated, leaving her feeling deeply hurt and depressed.

She moved closer to the river, which was frozen at the edges, but was too deep and fast flowing to freeze over completely. She had heard that further downstream, several inches of ice formed on the surface with the water moving underneath, but here the constant flowing of water was hypnotic. There were few rocks at this spot and the water rushed by, grey, sullen and uncompromising. Its power was frightening and awe inspiring at the same time.

It would be so easy to take a few more steps and sink beneath the surface. Then all her problems would disappear. But she could not do that. She had been brought up to think suicide a mortal sin. Still the water drew her. Would it be a sin if she just fell in? Suddenly a voice interrupted her thoughts.

'Granny, your nose is frozen.'

She turned and saw a boy about her own age standing next to her. She took off her glove, rubbed her nose to bring life back into the frozen flesh, and then was filled with anger. Granny! How dare he call her granny! He was the same age as her. In that moment, she knew she would continue to fight. She would not let a quarrel get her down. Tomorrow she would go to the hospital and she would be cured. She would ignore Stasia and Lucia until they saw sense. She made a rude sign at the boy and walked purposefully back to the dugout.

Worn out after her argument, Halina slept until the next morning. Stasia and Lucia were sitting by the stove when she woke, but she decided she would ignore them and eat her breakfast in silence. Every now and then, she saw Lucia looking at her, and once Stasia started to say something, but she would not give in. She would stick to her campaign of silence until she was about to leave.

'I am going to the hospital now,' she said as she opened the door to the dugout. Perhaps they would apologise to her now.

There was no response.

The journey to the hospital was more difficult than that to the clinic and Halina had to stop and rest several times. It was very cold, but it had stopped snowing and the sun gave the illusion of warmth. What could she think of this time to forget how tired she was? Memories swirled and danced before her, but the memory that opened up was an unexpected one. Years before when she was seven or eight, Papa had taken her on a horse drawn sleigh past the edge of a hill favoured by skiers. It was the Christmas holidays and one of the few times in the year when he had free time for her. It had been a bright sunny day and the sun had reflected off the snowy fields around. Every now and then a skier had flashed past calling a cheery greeting as their tracks carved a shallow furrow in the crisp snow.

Everything seemed so clear in her memory now. She could even see the breath

174

from the horse rising up in clouds and weaving a misty path between the sleigh bells. The sleigh ride had been part of her Christmas present, but of course, the best part of the present had been to spend time alone with Papa. On this occasion, he had seemed happy in her company, waving a greeting to familiar faces as they criss-crossed in front of them. How could she forget that time? Those were the days before he had started disciplining her and she had not felt resentful and upset. But those were also the days before she had started being defiant. She had never learned the right way to talk to Papa. Ola was much more successful.

She stopped in surprise. The hospital. She had arrived already.

Halina walked in and handed over the documents given to her by the clinic, to a rather harassed-looking nurse wearing a uniform that was stained and worn-looking. 'We are very busy,' she said. 'We have a lot of sick here. There are outbreaks of malaria and typhus. You will have to wait.'

She sat on a cracked wooden chair in a corner and waited. Someone came past with a trolley and she managed to beg some soup and a little bread from her. The auxiliary must have decided she looked ill and was entitled to it, as she did not even argue when she asked. As she waited, several patients came in to the hospital and she began to regret having eaten. One was throwing up constantly and another was covered in blood, having had some kind of accident in the oil fields. It was very off-putting. She would have to study her fingernails every time she heard another casualty approaching.

After three hours and a welcome gap in new entrants, she finally was admitted. She was taken to a steam bath, and told to wash thoroughly. Her clothes were taken away 'to be disinfected' and she was given a hospital tunic. It was too big. Did they not have anything in her size? She would have to lift it up as she walked to prevent tripping over it. She was given a bed in a large ward, where she was seen by a doctor who read the notes from the clinic and gave her a cursory examination. Afterwards he was silent. What did that mean? Perhaps she should have asked him, but he looked so forbidding and she did not want to annoy anyone.

The ward was nothing like the clean fresh-smelling room she expected from a hospital. The beds were very close together and the floor and walls were none too clean. What was that scuttling under the bed opposite? Better to ignore it. Pretend it was not there. She lay back on the hard pillow and drew the thin blanket up around her chin. At first she found lying in the bed comfortable and she played out scenes in her head where she would be given a magic potion to cure her of all ills. Surely hospital was the place to be?

As the day wore on into night, the dream turned into a nightmare.

Several of the ward inmates moaned and cried out at intervals. Some made noises Halina did not want to investigate too closely and she tried putting her fingers in her ears. Nurses came and went in the ward, and she noticed that the person two beds away from her, was getting a lot of attention. She had been moaning quite loudly and a makeshift curtain was pulled round her bed. After a while, two men came in with a stretcher and left carrying a shape covered with a sheet. It was a dead body. She had seen the same thing at the labour camp. A few hours later, another woman started crying out that she could not breathe. Her gasping breaths continued for several hours before it became obvious, that she had died. Why was she in here? She was not as ill as they were. She was not going to die. Was she?

It was terrifying. She had never before seen or heard someone die. She had been to funerals and even seen several dead bodies wrapped in cloth in the camp, but actually hearing someone die…. she could not bear it. She turned over, covered her ears and tried hard to think of something pleasant, but as soon as she started to drift off to sleep and welcome oblivion, another person would start crying or choking. She would never forget those awful sounds. Why was the night so long?

In the morning, another doctor came to see her. He was even older than the doctor at the clinic, and said nothing to her as he examined her. When he had finished he spoke to a nurse who came over to her.

'There is nothing we can do for you here,' she said in a sharp clipped voice. 'You are going to die anyway and we need the beds for people we can help. You will have to go. Someone will bring your clothes.' With that, she turned and left.

Halina was truly numbed by what the nurse had said. She had been so sure that she could be cured, that as soon as she had someone to care for her and feed her well, she would recover. She was too young to die. She must see her family again. An auxiliary nurse brought her clothes a short while later, and put them on the bed. Halina tried to find out why she could not stay, but all the nurse said was, 'We need the beds. There are many sick Russians this winter.' Her emphasis on the word Russian spoke volumes. She was Polish and until recently the enemy. She was too low down the list for them to care about.

She sat on the chair near the hospital exit. A nurse came along the corridor and told her again that they could do nothing for her. 'You are going to die anyway,' she said, 'There is no point in you coming here. You cannot take a bed for someone who might be saved. You must go.'

Halina looked out at the snow-covered path. It was warm where she was and it was cold outside, but somehow she had to get back to the dugout. She rose slowly to her feet. Her melancholy was so great she hardly noticed her pounding headache. The thought of dying itself was not her greatest fear - it some ways it would be relief from the weakness that dominated her every move. But to die without seeing her family again? If she died there in the hospital, they might just throw her body out into the snow for the wolves.

The nurse stood holding the door open and looked pointedly at her. She limped slowly through the door, which was closed firmly behind her. How was she going to get back to the dugout? She was tired and depressed and could not imagine walking the three miles back. As she stood by the side of the road, she thought she heard the sound of sleigh bells. Sleigh bells at Christmas? It must be her imagination again. However, slowly round the corner, came a sleigh piled high with logs and pulled by a thin brown horse. It was a miracle. The sleigh stopped next to her. She looked up and saw a lined brown face just visible above a thick brown scarf. The face belonged to a man who looked about sixty. His breath escaped in silver white puffs as he spoke.

'Where are you going?' he said, 'Can I help'.

Had she really heard him say that? It was too good to be true. 'I have lodgings three miles from here on the other side of Barnaul,' she said, 'a dugout near the river. It belongs to a stoker.'

'Climb up,' he said kindly, 'I think I know that place. I'll take you there.'

Halina leaned weakly against the side of the sleigh. 'Thank you so much,' she said, trying to climb on board. Her benefactor, realising that she was too weak, jumped down and lifted her onto the sleigh.

176

'They say I am going to die,' Halina said, 'but I don't want to die in the street.'

'Miracles can happen, do not give up hope yet.' With that, he shook the reins and the horse plodded slowly along the road.

'You are very kind,' she said. 'Thank you.'

'I am going your way. Besides, I have a granddaughter your age. I would not want her to be left by the side of the road. You look as if a snowflake would flatten you. Are you from Moscow?'

Halina could not believe what she had heard. The Russian she had been taught by Maria was grammatically perfect and no doubt had a Moscow accent, but it was strange to be mistaken for Russian.

'No, I am Polish. I am staying with two other girls. We were released from the labour camp a few months ago.'

As they drove, the driver asked Halina questions about Poland, and how she had come to Russia. His kindly interest continued as they travelled through the town. He appeared to be better off than many of the Russians she had seen, and it seemed he had a younger brother in the Red Army. 'Fighting the Germans somewhere.'

Arriving at the dugout, Josef, as she discovered he was called, helped her down from the sleigh and watched as she walked the last few steps to the dugout.

'Halina, what are you doing here,' Lucia and Stasia came rushing forward as Halina entered.

'They told me they could do nothing for me and that I am going to die,' Halina said.

The tears, which had been held back so long, started to run down her face. She lay on her side on the bed and wept as her friends, past quarrels forgotten, stood by uncertainly. She was glad that they had been proved so very wrong. It would be some time before she completely forgave them for their earlier unkindness.

'What are we going to do,' asked Lucia.

Halina did not answer. She had even forgotten that it was Christmas day.

Thirty Nine

Halina, December 1941, Barnaul District

The next few days were difficult for everyone. Halina was depressed and trying to come to terms with the hospital's diagnosis, and the others were still feeling guilty and afraid to say much to her. She lay in bed most of the time, only getting up to eat and when she had to, but on days she did not feel much worse, she got up and went for a short walk outside if it was sunny. She needed fresh air. She would still recover. She was sure of it. The hospital must have got it wrong.

When next she saw Stasia and Lucia, they came excitedly into the dugout after their nightshift. It was early morning and Halina was awake, lying with her eyes closed, trying to decide if she had the energy to get up.

'Halina,' Lucia came up and shook her gently, 'We have some fantastic news for you. We saw a notice in the post office in Barnaul. There is a Polish Relief Office near Barnaul and they are here to help released Polish deportees and prisoners, which means us. We have got the address and can take you there this morning.'

It was wonderful news. At last she was to get some help so that she could leave this terrible place. Immediately Halina felt her depression lift and she forgot that she was still upset by her friends' earlier behaviour. She got up, dressed and stood by the stove, trying to come to terms with things. She would actually be leaving. Going back to Poland. Wonderful news, but….

Halina sat down on the stool. But her hopes had been raised many times before and dashed just as often. The hope of escaping to Warsaw, ended in arrest, the hope of improved conditions in Siberia had been cruelly dashed. She leaned forward towards the heat. She had been rather stupidly optimistic there. There was the euphoria at being set free from the labour camp, but here she was, still stuck in Russia with her health going down the drain. The visit to the hospital had been full of hope only to be replaced with a death sentence. How could she be sure this latest bit of hope would be fulfilled? She took the drink Stasia had offered her. If she hoped too much, she would be even more disappointed if this latest dream turned out to be a nightmare like all the others. She muttered a few choice Russian swear words under her breath. Her health, her wretched, damned, health.

Stasia and Lucia were looking at her, expecting her to be as happy as they were. She took a sip from the cup. 'It is such fantastic news,' she said, forcing her mouth to smile, 'It takes a bit of getting used to.' Her optimism trumped her and she felt happy despite herself. What was the point of being negative? Better to enjoy the moment.

An hour later, she was tucked up on the sledge they had brought from the old cottage. Stasia and Lucia took turns pulling her, and together they trudged the four miles to the relief office. It was such a relief that they were being so sympathetic and had gone to the trouble of covering her in blankets and making sure she was comfortable. She simply could not have walked four miles. The ride was bumpy, but as they approached the relief office, Halina saw a Polish flag above the door of the building. A Polish flag after all this time. Polish aid workers really were here in Barnaul. At last, at long last the nightmare was over. She could feel tension leaving her body as her worries drained away. Now she had to stop herself crying and making a fool of herself. All those doubts she had earlier were just silly. Probably caused by her fever. It would be so wonderful to hear a friendly Polish voice.

The relief worker was very kind and patient and after hearing their stories, he immediately promised that they would have help to leave Russia once they could organise it. Halina was given extra money so that she could buy food. 'It is possible that your problems are caused by poor food,' the relief worker explained, 'We have seen so much of it. Hopefully the money will buy you some decent quality food and you will feel much better, but if not,' at this point he paused and smiled kindly at her, 'if you find you are not improving please come back and we will try to arrange something else. We may have a doctor by then.'

She glanced at Stasia and Lucia who faces were glowing with excitement. They had been kinder to her, but she knew now they saw her as a burden. That much was clear. They made their way back to the dugout in high spirits, stopped at the market and tried to buy as much as they could of the food recommended by the relief officer, at the same time rationing the money he had given, so that it would last several weeks. Back at the dugout, Stasia cooked a meal for her while she lay in bed. She was obviously feeling guilty. However, she would not forget that Stasia had betrayed her.

Two hours later, much of the food passed straight through her.

Several weeks went by, but Halina realised she did not feel any better. With the money she had been given, she could afford much more nutritious food, so why was she still feeling weak? She still had frequent headaches, fevers and diarrhoea, and could scarcely lift one foot in front of the other. She would have to go back to the relief office. She tried to stop fear from ambushing her. Surely this would not be yet another disappointment?

Much less resentful, Stasia and Lucia took her back to the relief office on the sledge, and this time she took her belongings with her. There would be no point in returning to the dugout until she felt less ill. Throughout the journey, she prayed silently to herself. Please God, this time, this last time, please see that my optimism is not shattered.

The doctor, who was Russian, not Polish, examined her briefly, and afterwards the relief officer came to see her. He was kind but Halina could see that he now believed what the hospital had said to her. 'It seems that you are not going to recover,' he said kindly, 'and in your present condition, there would be no point in putting you on a train out of Russia. Conditions on the journey would be difficult and as you are so ill now, you would not make it. After I saw you last we made enquiries and there will be a place for you in an Old People's Home in Bijsk.' He saw Halina's expression and added hurriedly, 'I know it is not ideal, but at least it will be peaceful. I will organise someone to accompany you there today.'

Halina felt crushed. Yet another hope had been trampled in the mud. This time there was nothing to rescue her. Just a bed in a building surrounded by old dying people.

'It will be the best thing for you,' said Stasia.

Halina felt her anger flare. Had she the energy, she would have told Stasia just what she thought of her selfishness. But what would be the point? It would not help. Perhaps she would do the same if the roles were reversed. She pulled her scarf round her head to hide the gathering storm of tears. Even her friends had disappointed her in the end.

Forty

Halina, January 1942, Soviet Russia

The Polish aid office sent a young assistant to travel with Halina to Bijsk. He helped her onto the train, practically lifting her onto her seat. After her previous experience of travelling in cattle trucks, she was pleased to see that she was in a railway carriage with seats.

'How long will it take us to get there,' she asked.

The assistant smiled kindly at her 'It will take most of the night,' he said, 'It is about 100 miles. Are you comfortable, can I get you another blanket or some water?'

Halina took a sip from the bottle of water handed to her, sank into the comfort of the seat, and looked out of the window. Perhaps she should be crying, but it would not do any good. She was going to die and that was that. Inside she felt very calm, almost as if she was watching someone else through a glass wall.

Lucia and Stasia had walked four miles in the snow to bring her to the Polish relief centre. They had helped her onto the sledge and wrapped her in blankets. It was obvious that they had started to feel guilty that they had not recognised how ill she was. Lucia, whose soft nature had only been thinly covered with a hard layer, was particularly contrite. She had spent ages tucking the covers round her, rather as her mother had when she was little. 'Hang on, Kasia,' she said, using the diminutive that her mother used, 'You are a fighter. Don't let it win.' But then they knew she was going and would not be a burden any more. They could afford the luxury of guilt.

Once they had delivered her, they had turned and left, it being too cold for them to wait around. The Polish aid office had given them a route to follow out of Russia and they were planning to leave by train in the next few weeks. They had met up with a few of the other girls from the camp and intended travelling together. She had been with them for nearly eighteen months, sharing memories, trials and tribulations and part of her was sad to see them go. However, there was only a small part left for such regrets. She was going to die without seeing her family again. That she could not bear.

It was already dark and the lanterns burning on the station illuminated the flakes of snow that were drifting down. It was probably well below freezing outside, but even the very basic heating on the train made the carriage seem almost warm and the blanket wrapped round Halina's legs completed her comfort. She looked at the battered little suitcase at her feet. All that she possessed in the world was in that case. She felt her eyes prick and shut her eyelids. She must not cry in front of the aid worker; she must at least retain her dignity. The train started to move and soon the rocking motion of the carriage sent her to sleep.

She woke after a short time as the train hurried though the frozen countryside, and looked at the window. All she could see was a distorted reflection of her face. Was that really her face? That pale, thin image framed by short hair. It looked like a stranger. It had stopped snowing, but there were piles of snow at the side of the track. She pulled the blanket more tightly round her. She had to try to be positive in her last few hours or days. At least she would be able to die in comfort in a bed and would not be thrown out into the snow.

She looked at the window again and suddenly the feelings she had been holding back, flooded over her. She could hardly breathe. She would never see Papa, Mama, or Ola again. She leaned her head against the back of the seat and watched her reflection as a large tear rolled down her face. Had she forgotten? She was not going to cry in front of the aid officer. She closed her eyes to trap the tears and tried to shut out the painful feelings. She felt herself gradually drifting off and she felt comfortable for the first time in a long time.

As she drifted, suddenly she heard her father's voice loudly calling her name. She opened her eyes with a start and looked across at her companion. Had he called her name? But no, he was sitting with his own eyes closed, his head weaving from side to side with the motion of the train. Had she really heard her father's voice? She tried so hard to concentrate that her head began to ache. The feeling that he was close was very intense. She remembered how angry she had been when she had last seen him, but that seemed so long ago now. After her experiences, she had learned just how important family was to her. Surely they would be more understanding with each other now? She would not get the chance to tell him that she loved him. She would never know for sure how much he loved her. That, more than anything, was what she wanted to hear before she died.

She leaned down to open her case and brought out the little tinderbox. She opened it, began the familiar ritual of tracing the edge of the flint with the tips of her fingers, and whispered her father's name and how much she loved him. The stone felt very warm. Has she really heard his voice? Was it in her head? In her conscience? Or had it really been his voice passing through the many miles that separated them? Did you hear me say I loved you Papa?

'That looks like an old fashioned tinder box.' Halina looked up to see that her companion was awake and watching her curiously.

'Yes it is,' she replied, 'it belongs to my father - he is an officer in the Polish army.'

'Tell me about your family,' he said, 'what part of Poland are you from?'

The aid worker talked to Halina in a kindly and gentle tone as he asked about her family. But she did not want to talk to him. It would lower her defences and remind her of what she had lost and would not see again. He asked again in a tone of gentle persistence. She turned to look at him. Perhaps it might help a little if she talked. It might be easier if she talked about times before the war. Talking of her father and mother might make them seem closer. Perhaps he realised how lonely she was.

And so she told him where she was born, of her time in Lwow, of her sister, of her mother, her beautiful mother. She discovered that the aid worker had been born not far from Wilno in Northern Poland, where she had been born. They talked of Polish food, and how much they missed it. She described how she had managed to avoid arrest by the NKVD and how her mother had to try to conceal that she was the wife of an officer.

'We thought we would be safe,' she continued, 'we were about to cross the border at the River Bug, but we were betrayed.' She told him about her time in prison, and how her mother had recited poems to help pass the time. 'She was so good at it,' she said, 'I almost felt as if I was somewhere else when she recited.'

Her companion told her that there was a Polish government-in-exile in London, where he had come from. 'Stalin has become an ally of Britain and America,' he said,

'General Sikorski was quick to demand that the Polish prisoners should be released as part of that alliance. And that is why we are here.' He described to her the difficulties of the relief workers. 'We have great difficulty finding out where everyone is. You may have noticed,' he paused to smile, 'that Russia is very large. Initially the NKVD helped us, but they are becoming a little less cooperative now. However, we think we have located the main centres where the labour camps are. There are just so many of them. In addition, some people were just deported, not sentenced to labour camps. Some have been working on the communal farms, the kolkhoz, or in the villages. Those in the farms often fared better as at least there was a source of food nearby. Unless of course they were made unwelcome by the Russians.'

Exhausted by the conversation, Halina closed her eyes. The aid worker had been patient and understanding and had listened attentively when she talked, then had talked himself when she fell silent. It had helped her a great deal. Perhaps by the time they arrived at Bijsk, she would feel more able to accept her fate.

Forty One

Eugenia, January 1942, Dzhalal-Abad

Eugenia hugged herself with excitement as she lay on her makeshift bed in the tent. In a few days she was travelling to northern Russia to look for Halina, So often she had asked, 'Have you seen my daughter?' and too often the reply was 'No.' Until last week. An aid worker returning with some refugees thought he had recognised the name on a list of survivors being cared for in a temporary aid camp in northern Russia. Immediately Eugenia had asked the camp leaders if she could have an escort to take her north. Normally such a request would have been refused, but Eugenia was so well loved in the camp and was so persuasive, that the General of the Division had promised an adjutant to help, despite the danger of travelling in the Russian winter.

And soon she was going. She had longed for this moment for every minute of her separation from Halina, but she could hardly believe it was about to take place. Soon she would be on her way.

Halina, January 1942, Bijsk

The relief worker helped Halina out of the train when they arrived at Bjisk station and supported her as they walked out of the station.

'The home does not open until ten am,' he informed her, 'and it is only five now, so I will take you to the Polish relief station until it is time. It is a short walk from here.'

Anything that would delay her arrival at the nursing home was worth using up some energy for. Somehow, she was able to walk the few hundred yards to the relief station, which consisted of several rooms in a small wood and stone building.

She sat on her suitcase in a corner near a stove, which was throwing out more heat than she had felt in a long time. It was such a relief that she had managed to travel to Bijsk without the embarrassment of frequent and urgent trips to the toilet. The medicine she had been given before her journey had helped settle her stomach. Someone gave her some bread and she chewed it thoughtfully. It was soft and fresh and so delicious. A Polish officer came into the room.

She sat, leaning against the wall. There would be peace and comfort awaiting her in just a few hours. Strange, but that was all she could think of now. Just how wonderful it would be to lie in a bed in peace and comfort. She heard voices and looked up, vaguely aware that someone was talking to the aid worker. She gave a start. Was that her father? It was the first Polish officer's uniform she had seen for two years and she remembered the last time she had seen her father in such a uniform on the day he had left to go to the war. But, it was not her father. Just a stranger.

The officer continued talking to the aid worker and she could hear her name mentioned several times, as the relief worker told him about her family background. He turned to look at her every few minutes, before asking more questions. Why was he so interested in her? She was just a thin, ill girl who had only a short time to live, surely that would not interest him. Eventually he came over to her, bowed and introduced himself as Captain Skrzydlewski. The sight of a uniform had awakened many memories, and she found herself rising to her feet as good manners taught in the past made her react without thinking. 'I am Halina Korbinska,' she said shaking his hand.

'Halina,' he said, 'I have been talking to the gentleman over there - he has told me about you.'

Halina looked at him blankly. Why should be interested in her? It did not make sense.

'Halina,' he said, his voice catching, 'Halina, I know your father - we were at officer training together.'

She stared at him unable to speak.

'Halina,' he continued, taking her hands as he said it, 'I know your mother. Your mother has already found the army in Uzbekistan - I know her - she is well. She has been looking for you and asking everyone if they have seen you.'

The world started to swim in front of her. Suddenly there were three or four people round her. She looked at the sea of smiling faces, which became whiter and whiter. She could feel her heart pounding and crashing in her ears and then she collapsed in a faint.

When she opened her eyes a few minutes later, she found the room full of people come to look at the little miracle. Cases appeared from nowhere and were put together to make a bed. Soup was brought to her, blankets were tucked round her. The overnight train journey had helped her come to terms with her fate, but now she had hope again. She had survived two years of deprivation, now she had hope. She had not realised just how much she had missed kindliness. She could cry now. It would not matter if she cried.

The officer's wife appeared at her side and Halina realised that she and her husband were speaking to her. 'We would like to take you with us,' they said, the tears in their eyes almost as large as Halina's. 'We know your mother is looking for you. We are travelling towards Tashkent and want to take you to see her.'

Halina simply could not take in this news. She must be dreaming again. It could not be real. She closed her eyes. When she opened them again it will have disappeared. She opened her eyes. Everyone was still there. It was real.

A female doctor appeared on the scene, and shooing the well-wishers out of the room, she examined her. 'Halina,' she said gently, 'you are suffering from pellagra. It is very common and we have found so many cases.' Halina looked puzzled and she explained, 'It is caused by lack of nutrition and especially vitamin B. That caused the rash you have and the diarrhoea. Unfortunately, you also may have malaria. There has been a dreadful epidemic of it in Russia. Most people think it is just found in the tropics but there is a strain which is found even as far north as Archangel.' She called the Captain and his wife back into the room and gently told them that Halina was very weak and ill and might die on the way to Tashkent. 'But if you want to take the risk, then you should take her.'

Halina did not have to think for a second. If she was going to die anyway, how much better it would be to die full of hope of seeing her mother again. Perhaps she would not die before she saw her. The couple saw the look on her face and did not hesitate. The soldier's wife took her hand and said gently, 'We want to take you with us, would you like us to?'

Halina could hardly speak but managed to whisper, 'Yes,' before the tears started

186

again. She was crying again. But, it was all right. Everyone else was crying too. Well-wishers surrounded her again, asking her about her experiences. The Captain and his wife did not let them stay long, saying she had to conserve her strength. She lay back in warmth and comfort listening to the gentle voice of the Captain's wife talking about her time on a kolkhoz and started to doze off. She was going to see Mama again. She was going to see Mama. Her dreams had come true at last.

Forty Two

Halina, January 1942, Soviet Russia

The Captain had brought with him a young soldier who was training to be an officer, and his role was to help the Captain with his wife, Zosia, and his two children. Because Zosia and her children had been on a communal farm rather than a labour camp, she had been able to write letters with more freedom, and the Captain knew where to come to find her when the amnesty was announced. His family now expanded to include Halina.

The first train arrived and Halina was wrapped in blankets and carried aboard. She looked around at the Pullman carriage in amazement. It was a revelation. Most of her train journeys in Russia had been in cattle trucks or similar, but this train had padded seats – luxury she had not seen in Russia. Zosia fussed round her making sure she was comfortable and warm. She was being treated like a baby and she loved it. To be treated with such love and kindness after so many months of hardship…. Halina brushed back yet another tear. Crying with happiness was a new experience.

The Captain explained to her how he knew her mother.

'Your mother is in the army now, with the 5th Polish Division,' he said, 'she is known by everyone. She is attached to the education department and is part of the newly formed theatre. Whenever she meets anyone new, she asks, "Have you seen my daughter? Where do you think she might have gone?" She knew you were in Starodub but did not know where you went once the war with Germany started.'

'When we were in prison my mother use to recite poems and plays to me,' Halina said, 'It helped me to forget we were in prison.'

The Captain nodded, 'Your mother is well known for her wonderful reciting. Having even a small theatre is so important for the morale of the men.'

Halina lay back and smiled as she thought of her beautiful mother reciting a romantic Polish poem and imagined the soldiers sitting spellbound. Soon she might be able to hear her too.

As the train powered its way south, Halina lay in comfort, half-asleep, half-awake. She knew she was very ill, but to have her worries removed and replaced with hope made her feel better. She might just stay alive long enough to see Mama. She must hang on until then. The train stopped at a main station and the Captain's aide carried her out wrapped in blankets, and sat her down in the station restaurant, although it could hardly be called anything so grand. The smell of the food was intoxicating – she had not seen so much food for a long time. She caught sight of her reflection in a mirror. Was that really her? She certainly looked on the point of death.

'The doctor told me what to feed you to help you get better,' Zosia said as she sat down. 'You might feel like eating a steak but you would not be able to digest it, so it is good quality soup and fresh vegetables or fruit for you, if we can get it.'

The food arrived, but Halina could not lift the spoon to her mouth without her hand shaking. She had become even weaker. Was that a bad sign? Zosia picked up her spoon, fed her, and held the cup while she drank. It was just as well she was enjoying being treated like a baby. A short time after the meal, she felt familiar pains in her stomach, and Zosia took her to the toilet. She realised with embarrassment that she had not quite managed to get there in time. Without hesitation and with great care and tenderness, Zosia helped her clean up.

'Just think of yourself as my baby,' she said, 'I did this for my babies so I can do it for you.'

It was such a relief to have someone to lean on, someone to help her, that Halina felt her blushes receding. It was almost like being with Mama again. She saw tears in Zosia's eyes as she looked at her skeleton-like arms and legs. 'How could they do this to a child,' she whispered to herself, unaware that Halina was watching her.

At times during the journey, Halina felt very ill with headaches and shivering or fevers, not to mention the familiar diarrhoea, but symptoms that only a few days ago threatened to engulf her, she managed to keep at bay. She had to stay alive long enough to see her mother. Time she put her fighting spirit to good use. To pass the time, she talked to Zosia about her experiences, and Zosia told Halina about hers.

'We were lucky,' Zosia said, 'We did not go to a labour camp but were sent to one of the collective farms. We managed to find an old couple whose sons had gone to fight, so there was room in their little wooden hut for us. The children went to school and I worked in the fields. It was such hard work, but at least we had food. The children had some food at school, so we did not starve. I had quite a few things with me that I managed to trade for food when things were scarce.'

Halina told her about Starodub and how they insulted Stalin for weeks before the guards realised what they were doing.

Zosia laughed at that. 'Such spirit! My children, alas, think Stalin is a good person, they were told so much at school. I will have to change that idea. Every now and then, they carried out this trick for the Polish children in the school. They would say to them, "Pray to your God for sweets." The children would pray and of course, no sweets came. Then they said, "Pray to Stalin for sweets," and when they did, sweets would fall from the ceiling. They had obviously rigged it up beforehand, but young children are taken in by such things.'

They told Halina that the journey would take ten days. It was such a long time. Would she last ten days? She just wanted to arrive whilst she still had a little strength. The captain and his wife were treating her with such love and kindness it was like heaven. Pray God the real heaven would wait just a little longer for her.

After ten long days, they arrived at their destination. The Captain was going on a little further to where his company was based, and when they arrived at the station, he found an ATS patrol and asked one of the privates if she would take Halina to her mother. Halina felt energised with excitement. This was it. She was here. Now she would see Mama. Tears started to flow again all round as she thanked the couple for their kindness. It had been such a miracle that she had met them. She struggled towards the ATS private who lifted up her case, and asked her if she would be able to walk to the camp. 'It is just five or ten minutes walk from the station,' she said. 'Your mother will be so happy to see you. It will be such a surprise for her, she has no idea you are coming. I know she is planning to go to look for you with a group who are going to northern Russia, but I do not think she has left yet.'

Halina did not even answer her and started to walk slowly in the direction she had indicated. She felt rather faint and dizzy. Was that her illnesses or just the thought of seeing Mama? They walked very slowly, but soon she saw lights and tents. Her heart started beating very quickly as she walked, and she was breathless by the time they stopped at one of the tents. The private lifted the flap and she could see beds inside with women sitting or lying on them.

And there was Mama.

'Giena,' shouted the private through the opening, 'I have your daughter here.'

Eugenia cried out, jumped off her bed and ran towards the tent door. Halina stood just inside the tent. Was she really here? Was it really her mother? Every now and then on the journey, there had been doubts and stabs of fear. What if it was not her mother? Perhaps someone else had the same name? But it was her. At last, at long last, she had not been disappointed.

Eugenia stopped and looked at Halina and the glow on her face slowly dimmed, as she looked at the bony, sick girl, whom she had not seen for a year and a half and who now stood in front of her. 'That is not my daughter,' she said and started to turn away dejectedly.

Panic seized Halina. 'Mama, Mama, it is me, Halina. Mama it is me,' she said, trying hard to shout with the little energy she had left.

Her mother turned back and looked closely at her, 'Oh Halina,' she said and folded her in her arms. At last, she was home.

Forty Three

Halina.
'Survival was the ultimate
defiance and she was the victor'

Eugenia, Halina, February 1942, Dzhalal-Abad

Eugenia picked Halina up and put her in her own bed, where she quickly fell asleep, exhausted by the emotional reunion. Janka, who had seen Halina arrive, stood next to Eugenia and hugged her. 'It is such wonderful news, Giena, I am so happy for you.'

'Keep an eye on her will you Janka, please. I must go and find the doctor.' Eugenia quickly pulled on her clothes and rushed into the night. The doctors in the camp were overworked and had too few supplies for the increasing number of refugees, but they would help her with Halina. She would make sure of it. The doctor on duty was quite young and already a little in love with Eugenia, as were many who had heard her recite. She had little trouble persuading him to examine the sleepy Halina. Afterwards he spoke to her outside the tent.

'I want to give you good news Giena, but it does not look promising. Halina has an advanced case of pellagra from malnutrition and has malaria. I am sorry to tell you, but those in her condition usually die as the organs in the body shut down. The malaria makes the situation much worse.'

Eugenia gripped his hand tightly, 'Please find a bed for her in the army hospital. Please tell me there is something I can do. I cannot sit by and watch her die. Not now I have found her again. Surely those people who die do not have a mother to give them constant attention?'

The doctor weighed his words carefully. He did not want to raise her hopes, nor did he want to disappoint her. 'You will have to watch her day and night, as if she were a baby. You will have to feed her pureed food and persuade her to drink constantly. Dehydration from the fever and the diarrhoea is the greatest danger. If you are prepared to do that I will try and find her a space.'

'I will do that,' said Eugenia and she rushed out to prepare some food for her daughter.

She felt so comfortable and warm. Whatever she was lying on was so soft. She half-opened her eyes and saw the face of an angel. It had happened then. She had actually died. Everything was so pleasant. It must be heaven. She closed her eyes, and then frowned a little. That face. The face of the angel. It was familiar, so familiar and loved. Her eyes sprang open and she saw a curtain of dark hair framing the face. Surely it was Mama? Was she in heaven too?

The angel spoke. 'Halina, how are you feeling? Are you all right?' That was Mama's voice. 'Mama? Is that you?' Her voice sounded strange and weak. Then she remembered. She had not died, she was in the Polish army camp and the night before she had been reunited with her mother. She closed her eyes again. It might be a dream. She must give way to sleep again. She must hang on to the dream.

She opened her eyes again, but this time she felt more awake. Dare she look? If it had been a dream, Mama would not be there. She had dreamed of her so often in the past, it might just be wishful thinking. She looked up, almost holding her breath. The face was still there.

'Halina can you drink this? You must replace the lost fluids. And you must eat. I have some pureed fish here. It has Vitamin B in it. You need that to get well.'

She took the drink offered, and managed a few spoonfuls of the fishy paste then looked at her mother's face. Still beautiful. There were lines she had not seen before, but the face was as she remembered. All those times lying in her bed in Starodub, holding the silken shawl to her nose, all those times lying in the dirt of Barnaul , this was the face that had kept her company. She reached up her hand to touch it. 'Mama I can't believe it is really you.'

'Yes, my dear, you are in the army hospital. You must drink this, Kasia,' said Eugenia using Halina's childhood name, 'You must eat and drink as much as you can, in order to get well. And you must fight, Halina. That is something you know how to do.'

Halina smiled a little, 'I will fight Mama, I have not fought so long just to give up now.' After taking more of the food her mother gave her on a spoon, Halina relaxed into her pillows and fell asleep.

Eugenia was so excited, so full of happiness. Her daughter had come back to her. A most wonderful gift. She stroked Halina's forehead and felt a little apprehensive. It was very hot. She still had a fever. But she could not lose her now, not just after she had found her. She would do any thing she could to make sure she lived. Those doctors did not know what a fighter her daughter was. She would not leave her side until she was well again. And she would be well again. Finding her had been such a miracle she could not die now.

For three months, Halina hovered between life and death, the fact that she had lived so long being a miracle according to the doctors. On several occasions, her fever rose dangerously high but Eugenia watched over her constantly, sponging her to lower her temperature. She used every ounce of her charm to obtain food from the most unexpected places. Good nutritious food was not in plentiful supply with refugees still arriving daily, but somehow she managed. She cajoled the doctors into giving Halina more than her fair share of care, and every day she fed her, washed her and dressed her. She rarely left Halina's side, encouraging as much fluid as possible into her, praying that any food that she managed to obtain would stay long enough inside to have the nutrients absorbed.

Slowly Halina began to recover, despite her prognosis. Once she was out of immediate danger, she was visited by soldiers and refugees alike. Everyone wanted to see Eugenia's miracle child – even the General of the Division came to see her. So many people had lost family and friends, the discovery of someone's long lost child was a cause for great celebration.

'Mama,' said Halina on several occasions, 'it is such a miracle that I found you. If I had not been too early for the nursing home, I would not have stopped and waited in the Polish Relief offices. If I had not talked to the aid worker about my family, he would not have known much about me. It was so amazing that a Polish officer who knew Papa was in the offices at the same time as me. I just cannot believe it.'

'And there is one more miracle,' added Eugenia, 'I was due to travel to northern Russia the day after you arrived. If you had been delayed for even a day, I would have missed you.'

Three months after being reunited with her mother, Halina sat in the audience as Eugenia gave a recital. Halina remembered the poems so well, but now they were a celebration of freedom, not a means to escape from hell. She sat bathed in a little of the warmth of the reception given to her mother, and thought how different the experience was from those days, years ago, when she sat behind the banisters listening to her mother playing the piano. The fact she was here at all, was due in some part to her stubborn, defiant nature, which had urged her through so many difficulties.

In the end, because she had survived, she had won a battle against those who had tried to take everything from her. Survival was the ultimate defiance and she was the victor. She smiled as she rose stiffly from her seat. Papa would be proud.

Ola, February 1942, Warsaw

The snow was falling in heavy, white flakes. Ola sat looking out at the snow with her paintbrushes forgotten on the table beside her. There were few people passing by, just the occasional soldier. Warsaw was a better place to be than Luck, she decided. Here at least they were not being hunted down and could live quietly without fear. For just now anyway. A fat flake hit the window and slid down gradually, its progress hindered by the frost patterns. Life was a matter of balancing things. Trying to balance the bad with some good. But getting a good balance had become more difficult since she had found the letter from Uncle Titov.

Ola.
'..all the paints in the world
could not balance the fact that
she had lost her family. '

She had just been looking in Aunt Janina's desk for a pencil sharpener and the letter had fallen out of the drawer. Well Aunt Janina shouldn't have left the drawer open. And once the letter was there she had to read it. Hadn't she? She breathed on the window and watched the warm patch start to melt the frost. Uncle Titov had said that Ukrainian guerrillas had killed Uncle Jan and Aunt Paulina the night after she had left them. Then he had added that because one of the members of the band had worked for Uncle Jan, there had been 'no torture or rape, Thank God'. She was not sure what it had all meant, but the nightmares had started up again. For two weeks she had woken up screaming at night. Aunt Janina had been very kind to her and had brought her the paints and brushes to cheer her up.

Now she felt a bit better, but working out the balance was a problem. Perhaps the fact that she had escaped from Brest balanced the fact that Uncle Jan and Aunt Paulina had been killed. She had lost her home in Kamionka, but that was balanced by being in Aunt Janina's house. All those bad months running from the NKVD had been balanced by her nice quiet life in Warsaw. She looked at the picture of Mama, Papa and Halina that she had painted that morning, and touched the faces lightly with her finger. Granny Korbinska had said she had real talent, so that was good. However, all the paints in the world could not balance the fact that she had lost her family.

Nothing could.

Epilogue

Halina 2010

Halina, January 2010, Devon, England

As I sit and think of my father, I remember the day when I walked into a Polish army shop. The war was coming to an end it was said, and I looked at the shirts and trousers on the shelves. We had sold all of Papa's things when we left Kamionka on our way to Luck. He would have nothing left when we saw him again. I bought a shirt and some trousers for him, happy that when he came home he would have something smart to wear. I kept that little parcel in my case for months and looked at it from time to time, thinking of my father and longing for the day when I would see him again.

However, my father never did come home. He died in a German prisoner of war camp, but not before we had received a letter from him, full of love for us all. I was able to write to him and tell him how much I loved him before he died, and that meant much to me.

For Poland, there was no miracle. Britain and America sided with our oppressor, Stalin, giving Poland into his control. We never could return home. Eastern Poland had become part of the Soviet Union, and we were too afraid to return to a Poland that was governed by communism. Later we discovered that killings and deportations carried on long after the peace treaties had been signed.

After the war, we came to England, where I live now. It hurt us greatly to be told not to talk of our experiences because the British government feared upsetting Soviet Russia. As a result, very few know the full story of Poland's past.

We were reunited with Ola some years after the war and marvelled at her own miraculous story. Mama and I met her, married and pregnant, when she came to visit us in England. We were overjoyed to find her, but after she had returned to communist Poland, I was left with the feeling that she had been more than a little scarred by her experiences. My own memories are softened by the intense feeling of joy I experienced when reunited with my mother. A feeling that is just as strong today. Poland was reborn with the fall of communism, and will always be in my heart, along with the memories of childhood, but to echo Ola's words, nothing can replace what we lost.

What would I want to be the reaction of those who read my story? It could be bitterness; but the flame of bitterness can burn those around you as well as yourself, and achieves nothing. It could be the desire for revenge; but millions of Russians and Ukrainians also suffered at the hands of the Totalitarian regime, and revenge is always destructive.

Perhaps what I would want them to feel is pride. Pride that their parents and grandparents endured with bravery the worst that man could inflict on man, pride at their deep devotion to Poland, pride in those who died in defence of their country. If one flame is to be fanned by reading these words, perhaps it should be the flame of patriotism. We cannot replace what we lost, but we can value what we have.

LaVergne, TN USA
03 January 2011
210846LV00002B/40/P